· · · · · · · · · · · · · · · ·

THE CURSE

. . . . . .

THE CURSE

· ·

A Cultural History of Menstruation

JANICE DELANEY
MARY JANE LUPTON
EMILY TOTH

A Sunrise Book
E. P. DUTTON & CO., INC.
NEW YORK

Grateful acknowledgment is given the following for permission to quote from copyrighted material:

Debbie Lempke, "The Bloods," from *The Berkeley Music Collective Songbook.* Copyright © 1974 by Debbie Lempke.

Lines from "She Shall Be Called Woman" are reprinted from *Collected Poems (1930–1973)* by May Sarton with the permission of W. W. Norton & Company, Inc., copyright © 1974 by May Sarton.

Nadine MacDonald, "On Menstruating in the Middle of a Lecture on the Fall of the Roman Empire," copyright © 1971 by Thomas E. Sanders. Reprinted from *Currents: Concerns and Composition* (Glencoe Press).

Portions of this book appeared in somewhat different form in *Rough Times* magazine and the *Women's Almanac.*

Library of Congress Cataloging in Publication Data

Delaney, Janice.
The curse.

"A Sunrise book."
Includes bibliographical references.
1. Menstruation. 2. Menstruation (in religion, folklore, etc.)
3. Menstruation in literature.
I. Lupton, Mary Jane, joint author.   II. Toth, Emily, joint author.
III. Title.
RG163.D44 1976   612.6'62   76-5461
ISBN: 0-87690-222-0

Published simultaneously in Canada by Clarke, Irwin & Company Limited, Toronto and Vancouver
Designed by The Etheredges

ACKNOWLEDGMENTS

Many generous people have contributed their information and insights to this book. While it is impossible to mention them all, we would like to thank the following people for their special help: Sarah Begus, Arthur Delaney, Dorothy Ginsberg Fitzgibbons, John Fitzgibbons, Genet Heiligh, Nancy Henley, Vickie Leonard, Richard A. Macksey, Elaine Markson, Mary Brown Parlee, May Sarton, James G. Sites, M.D., Marion Kelly, Bruce Toth, Aimee Wiest, J. J. Wilson, and Jane Yates.

CONTENTS

. . . .

THE CURSE

INTRODUCTION

In the beginning, the menstrual process inspired fear and wonder in human beings. Both men and women saw at once that woman's blood set woman apart from man in a mysterious, magical way. This blood flowed but did not bring death or disability; it came and went with a regularity that no human act could change. Only an even greater mystery, the creation of human life, could alter its pattern.

To reduce the threat of destruction by the unseen forces that directed woman's bleedings, early man at first made the womb a goddess. Worship and appeasement of the Great Mother and her bleeding fertility would ensure his temporary safety. Later, when farming began to replace hunting and gathering in the primitive economy, relative stability permitted man to use more direct ways to isolate the menstruating woman. So he made her taboo. The very word may originate in a Polynesian word for menstruation: *tupua*. In early agrarian societies, on the premise that menstruation empowered a woman to cause economic disaster, she was excluded from social and sexual intercourse for the duration of the menses; menarcheal girls underwent a pubertal seclusion that might last a few days, a few months, or a few years.

In our own culture, specifically twentieth-century America, women continue to suffer the taboos of centuries. Law, medicine, religion, and psychology have isolated and devalued the menstruating woman. Women who experience debilitating mental or physical pain at menstruation (despite the easy availability of The Pill and other such remedies) are made the prototype for all; and in the face of statistics to the contrary, women are still considered unreliable workers and unstable human beings at that time of the month. Thus, menstruation is a factor in the control of women by men not only in ancient and primitive societies, where knowledge of physiology is rudimentary at best, but also in our post-industrial world. Women are physically and emotionally handicapped by menstruation, goes the argument, and therefore cannot and may not compete with men.

Even literature has been silent on menstruation, probably because most "literature" has been written by men. To write about menstruation in myth, poetry, fiction, drama, and folktale is to write an essay about disguise and displacement, as the taboos of prehistory find continued expression in modern European and American culture.

To be sure, things are changing. There's a new freedom in the air, on the television screen, in the courts. Women writers and artists are bringing menstruation itself out of the water closet and using it as an emblem of celebration, not shame. We can thank the new feminism for helping us see that our concerns are of equal worth in the marketplace of ideas. And we believe that by approaching the subject "woman" through the most elementary and obvious aspect of womanhood, we will give our sisters a new respect for what has been, for most, a friendly monthly nuisance.

Part One

THE TABOOED WOMAN

. . . .

Chapter 1

WOMEN IN THE CLOSET: TABOOS OF EXCLUSION

Greater than his fear of death, dishonor, or dismemberment has been primitive man's respect for menstrual blood. The measures he has taken to avoid this mysterious substance have affected his mealtimes, his bedtimes, and his hunting season; and primitive woman, unable to separate herself from her blood, knew that upon her tabooed state depended the safety of the entire society.

Taboos exist to protect human beings from danger. Franz Steiner says that taboo deals with "the sociology of danger itself" because it is concerned with both the protection of dangerous individuals from themselves and the protection of society from them.[1] In many societies, the menstruating woman is believed to emit a *mana,* or threatening supernatural power. The taboos of menstruation are practices that help others to avoid her and her dangerous influence and that enable her to get through the menstrual period without succumbing to her own deadly power.

Menstrual taboos are among the most inviolate in many societies. How did woman come to merit this dubious privilege? Fear of blood, says Freud, who states furthermore that the blood phobia may also "serve aesthetic and hygienic purposes." [2] Thus, it was probably in the interests of cleanliness that a New Guinea Mae Enga tribesman known to the anthropologist M. J. Meggitt divorced his wife because she had slept on his blanket while menstruating and, still feeling not quite safe from her evil influence, later killed her with an ax. [3] Theodor Reik agrees with Freud's idea that the origin of menstrual taboos lies in the ambivalent attitude toward women in the most "advanced" cultures. He believes that the taboos are both a recollection and a denial of an earlier stage in society when women, like animals in heat, gave off a sexual signal at menstruation. Thus, he says, "the psychological quintessence at the root of the dread of menstruating women is . . . the unconscious attraction they exert on men and the power of the opposite feeling restraining them." [4] In the same vein, another anthropologist writes of the dualism implicit in woman's social position: "From one aspect the woman who may not be approached is inviolable, holy; from another aspect she is polluted, unclean. She is what the Romans called *sacra*, sacred and accursed." [5] Mary Chadwick, who in 1932 wrote the first full-length psychological study of menstruation, puts a similar idea more directly, referring to the "discomfort of guilt arising from instinctual wishes." [6]

Still other observers have reached into prehistory to seek a different etiology of these taboos. Bruno Bettelheim and others suggest that childbearing and menstruation were once a source of envy to men, who imposed the taboos in an attempt to equalize the sexes. [7] Elizabeth Gould Davis, who theorizes that matriarchies were the world's first political systems, sees the female-blood taboo as a vestige of the time when the ruling women used the taboo to make men respect and fear women. She cites the crime of matricide, the most serious even in patriarchal civilizations, as evidence in support of her theory. The tales of danger to men from women's blood, she says, "were tales told by primordial matriarchs to scare little boys into obedience and respect for women." [8]

There is as yet no direct evidence in anthropological literature that menstrual taboos originated with one or the other sex. A 1961 cross-cultural study of menstrual taboos found no relation between the extensiveness of such taboos and the importance of women's subsistence work or status in any particular society.[9] We believe, from the available evidence, that the taboos as taboos were probably enforced by men, who connected this mysterious phenomenon with the cycles of the moon, the seasons, the rhythm of the tides, the disappearance of the sun in nightly darkness and who feared such cosmic power in the apparent control of a member of their own species.

Each primitive society has tended to make the threat of menstrual pollution as concrete as possible. Therefore, to the Maori of New Zealand, the dreaded *kahukahu* contained in the menses is the personification of the germs of a human being and is capable of inflicting the most extreme harm on men.[10] The Mae Enga believe that contact with menstrual blood or a menstruating woman will "sicken a man and cause persistent vomiting, 'kill' his blood so that it turns black, corrupt his vital juices so that his skin darkens and hangs in folds as his flesh wastes, permanently dull his wits, and eventually lead to a slow decline and death." [11] The Tinne Indians of the Yukon Territory believe that menstrual blood contains the essence of femaleness; thus, menstruating women must avoid all contact with men, especially young men, lest they threaten their virility.[12]

To be sure, the magical nature of menstrual blood has some helpful aspects. Menstrual blood has been known to cure leprosy, warts, birthmarks, gout, goiter, hemorrhoids, epilepsy, worms, and headache. It was effective as a love charm, could ward off river demons and other evil spirits, and was occasionally fit to be an honorific offering to a god. The first napkin worn by a virgin was to be saved for use as a cure for the plague. But for most people, menstrual blood remained as the Roman Pliny described it in his *Natural History:*

> Contact with it turns new wine sour, crops touched by it become barren, grafts die, seed in gardens are dried up, the fruit of trees falls off, the edge of steel and the gleam of ivory are dulled, hives of bees die, even bronze and iron are at once seized by rust, and a horrible smell fills the air; to taste it drives dogs mad and infects their bites with an incurable poison. . . . Even that

very tiny creature the ant is said to be sensitive to it and throws away grains of corn that taste of it and does not touch them again.[13]

Equivalent beliefs persist to this day. No woman was employed in the opium industry in Saigon in the nineteenth century because it was believed that the opium would turn and become bitter if a menstruating woman was near.[14] Women in the 1920s widely believed that a permanent wave would not take if they were menstruating. Musicians are likely to blame broken violin and harp strings on their wives' menstruation. And most of us still consider it unlucky to walk under ladders, a superstition derived from the primitive world, where people would not pass under bridges, clotheslines, trees, or the like if a menstruating woman was about, lest some of the blood or its mana fall on their heads.

In many primitive societies, the menstruating woman was excluded from the most ordinary life of her tribe for four or five days every month. Unable to plant, harvest, cook, associate with her husband, or wander freely around the village, the woman went instead to the menstrual hut, a cramped dwelling of leaves and bark, set at some distance from the village. There a menstruating woman might, depending upon her culture, be required to undergo purifying practices or simply enjoy the solitude. In the latter sense, some anthropologists have seen the huts as an expression of a culture's need to establish privacy. But perhaps a better perspective on menstrual seclusion is given by Margaret Mead. She reports that the mountain Arapesh of New Guinea have a remarkable freedom from menstrual pain, "possibly because the extreme discomfort of sitting on a thin piece of bark on the damp, cold ground in a leaky leaf-hut on the side of a mountain, rubbing one's body with stinging nettles, obscures any awareness." [15]

The ethnologist A. E. Crawley explains the hut phenomenon and the periodic segregation of the sexes in terms of the primitive belief in the evil eye. Comparing such people to ostriches, who bury their heads in the sand to avoid an aggressor, he notes that to the primitive mind, the sight of a dangerous thing is the same as being seen by it.[16] If the dangerous menstruating woman is removed to a place where she can neither see nor be seen by the tribe, they will be assured of freedom from her mana as long as she is so secluded.

Such an extraordinary collection of taboos, taken with deadly seriousness by most of the world, throughout most of history, tells us a great deal about our psychosexual selves. Because the societies combed by the social scientists have been ruled by men, the mana of a menstruating woman was generally believed to be most dangerous to men; and on the conscious level, the taboos seem to aim more for the protection of men than of women. Now, women and men get together in two basic ways: through sex and through food. In both instances, woman provides a service to man that he cannot do without. Thus, the dangers to men (and because we are generally talking of patriarchies, the dangers to the whole society) from menstruating women must be mitigated by means of the strictest possible taboos regarding food and sex.

It should be noted that food taboos are not restricted to menstruating women. Food taboos were useful in preserving a society's totemic animals, in preserving the plants and animals most important to the economy of the group, or in teaching the society how to govern itself; perhaps, because food was undoubtedly the first form of property, the first human laws were these food restrictions, imposed and maintained by the tribal authorities. Although such food taboos continue today in some contemporary religions, the taboos associated with the handling of food by menstruating women have generally ceased to be observed in industrialized countries. But this is a relatively recent development. In most primitive societies, and some advanced ones as well, we find menstruating women tabooed from influencing the hunting, growing, preserving, cooking, serving, and enjoyment of food.

The cycle of food taboos begins with the hunt. Eskimo believe that contact with a menstruating woman can lead to bad luck in hunting; the contamination takes the form of an invisible vapor which attaches itself to the hunter so that he is more visible to game and therefore unable to catch it.[17] Among the Habbe of the western Sudan, a man whose wife is menstruating does not undertake any hunting.[18] Bukka women may not go into the sea to bathe for fear of spoiling the fishing.[19] The Sekani Indians of British Columbia gave menstruating women only dried meat or fish to eat because eating fresh game would spoil the hunter's luck.[20] Hays writes that the Melanesian Ifaluk Islanders have a "free and cheerful sex life . . . uncorrupted by any missionary teaching" [21] but nevertheless observe menstrual taboos to the extent that during the fishing season the men must live in the canoe house and abstain from women. Today's hunting lodge, that no-woman's-land of whiskey and Winchesters, echoes these primitive taboos.

Besides being dangerous to hunters and the hunt, menstruating women were considered capable of contaminating growing plants. This must have presented a worrisome contradiction to early peoples. The first objects of worship on this planet were probably women, in whom the principle of fertility was most clearly evident; the feasts of the Corn Goddess in ancient Europe indicate the inseparable linking of women and agriculture. Women were responsible for the cultivation of the fields; men went after the game. And women played key roles in the fertility rites of Demeter and Dionysus, in myth and in actuality. Women's success in agricultural labors was probably attributed to their obvious fecundity and was thought to be, like the power of childbearing, inherent in their sex.

But the power to create suggests the power to destroy. If woman could make things grow, she could also make them wither on the vine. Menstrual blood, the outward sign of her duality, could be her weapon to annihilate the society she was responsible for preserving. Thus, menstruating women of the Australian Arunta tribe are not permitted to gather the irri-akura bulbs, a staple of their diet, lest the bulbs fail. In Malekula, one of the New Hebrides islands, neither a menstrous woman nor her husband may enter a garden where young plants are growing. A woman of the Toradja people of central Celebes must avoid tobacco fields if her skirts are stained with menstrual blood, lest she blight the crop (but the same stained garment will keep the pigs out of a rice field).[22] Even in this century peasants in Italy, Spain, Germany, and Holland believed that flowers and fruit trees withered from contact with a menstruating woman. And Jewish women have traditionally been forbidden to plant during their periods.

Menstruating women are supposed to have an especially baneful effect on food when it is halfway between one state and another. Peoples in southeastern Europe, for example, will not permit them to salt or pickle because of the belief that the preserving will not take. This belief must have been brought to America early, for we have heard that it persists among some Kentucky coal mining families. The presence of a menstruating woman will prevent a French housewife from achieving a successful mayonnaise and will have an equally bad influence on cider being fermented, sugar being refined, and bacon being cured.[23] The peasants of Eastern Europe know that a menstruating woman must not bake bread or churn butter.

In an attempt to give scientific support to these beliefs, Bela Schick (1920) and David Macht (1924) separately observed, they said, the detrimental effect of menstruation on plant life. In one of Schick's experiments, a servant girl was given a bouquet of roses during her period; by the next day, the plants had faded. Schick coined the term *menotoxins* to describe noxious plant-destroying substances exuded through the skin of menstruating women. He added that menotoxins prevent dough from rising and beer from fermenting.

Macht discovered, he said, that menstrual blood had the power to inhibit the growth of plants. Moreover, it was not only the blood itself that had this power; as with Schick's servant girl, the menotoxic action could also be exercised through saliva, urine, perspiration, milk, tears, and even the air breathed by the menstruating woman.[24] However, two other researchers, attempting in 1934 to duplicate Macht's experiments, could not do so. In their results, nonmenstruating women had higher "toxic" scores than the menstruators did, suggesting, if anything, that women are are less foul during their periods.[25]

In 1950, Olive Watkins Smith and George Van S. Smith studied what they called *menotoxin*, a substance in menstrual blood that could cause death within a day if injected into an immature rat. However, Smith and Smith said that the substance was simply an "atypical globulin." It was toxic to immature rats only and had no effect on human beings or, apparently, on flowers.[26]

Even without the benefits of "scientific" research, the Carib of British Guiana have long known that a man who eats food prepared by a menstruating woman will never be well,[27] the Kharwar of India keep menstruating women out of the kitchen altogether,[28] and Ugandans damn the expense and destroy the family cooking pots during the housewife's menstrual period.[29] Iatmul are less rigid; in that tribe, a menstruating woman will not cook for her husband "unless she is out of temper with him and wishes to do him some mild harm." [30] The most ordinary of condiments, salt, comes under special prohibition for menstruating women in many societies. Sir James Frazer notes that in Central Agoniland a woman may cook for her husband while she is menstruating; but if she adds salt to his food, she will give him a disease called Tsempo.[31] In many preliterate societies, salt is connected with sexual intercourse and must be avoided when continence is necessary. Because there is no greater deterrent to sexual intercourse than menstruation, salt and sex must be avoided together.

A menstruating woman does not cease being a danger to food once it reaches the table. Theodor Reik recalls an incident that occurred when he was five and visiting his grandparents in Austria. His grandfather said, *"Mach den Tische rein!"* ("clean the table") to his grandmother. She left because she was *niddah* ("menstruating"), a term that comes from the verb *nadah* ("to expel").[32] In general, moreover, women and men observe some ritual separation at meals, whether they be peoples who fear the mana of the menstrual blood, peasants who assume that the wife serves the husband but does not sit herself, or ladies who withdraw while the men enjoy brandy and cigars. Crawley suggests that the origin of taboos against men and women eating together is "a form of egoistic sensitiveness with regard to the most important vital function" and can also be seen as a source of reinforcing sexual identity. Eating together is more usually seen, however, as a source of contamination to the male because food is commonly believed to acquire the properites of the person eating or serving it. Thus, the contact of food "with the person or influence of the female, transmits to the male the properites of women." [33] Hays tells of the decline of the Polynesian taboo civilization in

Hawaii in 1819 after a "strong-minded" wife of Kamehameha the Great saw European women enjoying banquets from which the Hawaiian women had been excluded and persuaded her husband to eat with the women of his family.[34]

In the United States today, outright cooking and segregation taboos are just a cultural memory. The emphasis is on behaving normally during the menstrual period, and be she housewife or career woman, or both, today's woman is determined to prove that she can do her job "like a man" even when she is feeling most like a woman.

Chapter 2

. . . .

"NOT TONIGHT, DEAR": TABOOS OF SEX

Food and sex are still inseparable as evidenced by the subtitle of a recent best seller: *The Joy of Sex: A Gourmet Guide to Love-Making*. Menstruation is listed in the table of contents under "Main Courses," instead of where we might expect to find it, under either "Sauces and Pickles" or "Problems." Dr. Comfort advises that this is a good time of the month to find variant sexual experiences; clothed intercourse and femoral intercourse (between the thighs) come highly recommended. In *The Sensuous Woman,* we find no such alternative. Avoid orgies during your period, "J" advises.

What is so remarkable about the sex taboos against menstruating women is that they have not faded into vestigial reminders of a primitive past; they are still very much a part of everyday life for most people. Thus, we cannot present this taboo in a vacuum, as a primitive curiosity; we must deal with it wherever it appears. It will readily be seen that the more sophisticated the society, the more scientific the explanation for the intercourse taboo.

We have already mentioned that the male treats the menstruating woman with ambivalence; he both envies her ability to create and fears her power to destroy. The love-fear relationship is nowhere so potent as when it involves the act of love itself. A man is as likely to be sexually aroused by a woman when she is menstruating as he is at any other time. But the blood of the menstruating woman is somehow dangerous, magical, and apparently not something he wants to get on his penis. It is thus necessary to protect the penis from the menses.[1]

Although the menstruating woman is still considered to be magical, the primary reason for the dread of intercourse during menstruation appears to be the blood itself, which has associations in the male mind with pain, death, battle, injury, and castration. It has been found that in those cultures where the intercourse taboo is most strictly enforced, there is a significant degree of castration anxiety (fear of losing the penis) among the males.[2] But official explanations for the intercourse taboo range from the holy to the hygienic, and they do not acknowledge that the male is afraid of *anything*.

IT'S AN OFFENSE AGAINST GOD

In certain patriarchal cultures, the dread that the male feels toward the menstruating woman becomes a part of his worship of his gods. In some societies, violations of sexual taboos are seen as sins against the god of fertility; in ancient Persia, the offense was so serious that it warranted burning in hell until Judgment Day. In the Koran, the sacred text of the Islamic religion, it is written: "They will also question thee as to the courses of women. SAY: They are a pollution. Separate yourselves therefore from women and approach them not, until they be cleansed. But when they are cleansed, go unto them as God hath ordained for you." Yet, in the Islamic account of the Creation, blood is seen, not as a source of pollution, but as the substance of creation: "Recite, thou, in the name of thy Lord who created;—/ Created man from CLOTS OF BLOOD:—/ Recite thou!" [3] Blood, like the menstruating woman, is *sacra*, both sacred and accursed.

The rule against intercourse with a menstruating woman in Judeo-Christian scriptures appears first in Leviticus 15:19: "And if a woman have issue, and her issue in her flesh be blood, she shall be put apart seven days: and whosoever toucheth her shall be unclean until the even." In Leviticus 20:18, the punishment is more severe than the curse of uncleanness until the evening. Here it is warned that *both* offenders "shall be cut off from among their people."

The taboo described in Leviticus is still observed among Orthodox Jews. If a bride is menstruating on her wedding night, one tradition requires that a little girl accompany her to the bridal bed lest the young lovers get carried away. There is evidently enough violation of the taboo to have prompted Isser Yehuda Unterman, chief rabbi of Israel, to issue a statement in 1972 on "Family Purity," a statement that goes to every couple in Israel who apply for a wedding license. In his pamphlet, Rabbi Unterman repeats the precautions against intercourse with a menstruating woman that appear in the Torah, and he recalls the punishment for violating the law, the penalty of *Karet*, the "cutting of life on earth and the denial of a life to come." Unterman tells of one woman who came to him with the complaint that despite her unclean state, her husband had forced himself on her sexually. The rabbi comments, "In my humble opinion, the cause of such unbridled behavior is due to modern conditions of life, which both incite and nauseate." [4]

IT'S BAD FOR YOUR HEALTH (HIS)

We have mentioned the Mae Enga belief that contact with a menstruating woman can make a man vomit, can "kill" his blood, waste his flesh, darken his skin, ruin his "vital juices," and "dull his wits." A South African clan believes that intercourse with a menstruating woman will make a man's bones get soft. In most cases, the punishment and physical suffering accompanying the violation of the intramenstrual taboo are borne by the male members of the community. That sexual intercourse during the period is of danger to *men* is the dominant belief of the forty primitive societies studied by William Stephens in 1961. It is also a dominant belief in European culture.

In the nineteenth century, it was widely thought that a male could get gonorrhea from contact with a menstruating woman. There seems to be a confusion between gonorrhea and such infections as trichomoniasis, both of which can be communicated to a man by a woman and vice versa. Trichomoniasis does become worse during menstruation because of lower vaginal acidity, but its most noticeable symptom is itching, not death, insanity, or worse. Augustus Kinsley Gardner, author of *Conjugal Sins* (1870), saw menstrual blood as corrupt and virulent, threatening an unwitting penis with "disease," "excoriations," and "blenorrhagias." ("Blenorrhagia" is now known as gonorrhea.) Another nineteenth-century idea was that the menstruating woman was likely, during intercourse, to regain from a man's lifeblood what she herself was losing.[5]

In the twentieth century, man's punishment from menstrual intercourse is said to be a disease called *urethritis,* an inflammation of the urethra, the duct that conveys both urine and semen. Such attacks are not very common, however; it is the rare medical practitioner who encounters a case. According to the best evidence available today, coitus during menstruation is perfectly harmless for men.

IT'S BAD FOR YOUR HEALTH (HERS)

If men are free from the dangers of soft bones, vomiting, or venereal disease during menstrual intercourse, women are similarly unthreatened. In fact, menstrual intercourse is good for women because it temporarily relieves cramps by increasing the flow. Yet, it has long been argued in medical circles that the combination of menstruation and intercourse is harmful for a woman. Soranus (second century A.D.) writes that it should be avoided because the uterus is already "overburdened and is in an unresponsive state because of the ingress of material and incapable of carrying two motions contrary to each other, one for the excretion of material, the other for receiving." [6]

A 1938 sex manual implies that during her period a woman is sick anyway and that she could get even sicker from indulging in sexual activities. "The female sexual organs are more or less congested, therefore more irritated and subject to pain, and vigorous sex relations would no doubt cause a

greater loss of blood by increasing the menstrual hemorrhage." [7]

Women seem to have accepted these pseudoscientific
taboos. In a study of 100 women conducted in 1950, most
reasons for abstinence listed by the participants had to do with
a fear that intercourse during menstruation would be physically harmful, that it might lead to "hemorrhage, injury, or
infection." [8] Even today, the most commonly argued reason is
medical: The woman does have a decrease in vaginal acidity
during her period and is at this time more likely to get vaginitis.

Among aboriginal peoples, a woman is occasionally in
real physical danger for having violated the intramenstrual
taboo. Among the Reindeer Chukchi, it was believed that a
woman would eventually become sterile because of such action. In anthropological writings, there is the rare example of a
woman suffering irregular menstruation as punishment for
having intercourse with a harmful "hot" male (one whose
blood is not cooled down). But this belief, found among the
Kgatia of Beuchanaland,[9] is the only example we could find in
any culture of a male's blood being the cause of a female's
illness.

The consensus of contemporary medical experts is best
expressed in this statement from a 1969 article: "There appears to be no established reason to abstain from coitus during
the menses on patho-physiologic grounds." [10] Those who do
abstain for such stated reasons are either ill informed or mask-
ing a deeper cultural dread of woman's blood.

IT'S BAD FOR YOUR HEALTH (THE UNBORN CHILD'S)

A lesser fear is that intercourse during menstruation can
harm the potential child. The Romans attributed the deformity
of the god Vulcan to menstrual intercourse between Juno and
Jupiter. In France, it was long believed that an infant conceived during the menses would be "puny, languid, and moribund, subject to an infinity of fetid maladies, foul and stinking
as a result of the matter from which it was conceived." The
child would be subject to a number of horrible diseases,

among them leprosy, syphilis, scrofula, and virulent ulcers of the skin. Mentally, it would be "entirely stupid, dull, loutish, silly, deprived of sense and understanding, and entirely unskilled to do anything good." [11]

We have found no medical evidence that a child conceived during the mother's menstrual period will be deformed, ulcerous, or rotten. Chances are, in fact, that neither a diseased child nor a healthy one will be forthcoming. One definite advantage to having intercourse during the menses is that it is "safe"; few women ovulate during days 1 to 5 of their cycle.

WOMEN ARE NOT AROUSED DURING THE PERIOD

Medicine and psychiatry have perpetuated the myth that women are the sexually passive members of the species and that they are the least interested in sexual activity while they are menstruating. Clinical studies usually show that the peak of a woman's sexual desire is during or immediately following ovulation. Fred Robbins stated in 1953 that the "menstrual blues" interfered with sexual desire.[12] Mary Jane Sherfey claims that women are most capable of multiple orgasms during the luteal, or postovulatory, stage; [13] Luschen and Pierce (1972) found, through studying women's reactions to pictures of sexually attractive males, that women are more easily aroused during ovulation than during menstruation.[14]

A few authorities are now beginning to recognize, however, that many women are most aroused during the flow itself. Masters and Johnson see arousal during the menses as an occasional happening.[15] This finding has been supported by others in the field. In still another study, 36 percent of the women noticed increased sexual desire during menstruation. "One patient reported that she experienced sexual desire only during menstruation, and on one occasion, felt so overwhelmed by passion that, although a shy and inhibited girl, she resorted to intercourse with a stranger." [16] Sexual arousal during menstruation has also been recorded among the Ngulu of eastern Tanzania. During her period, a Ngulu woman is "thought to attain her peak of fertility and passion," writes one anthropologist, "but precisely for this reason, men should avoid her." [17]

Not all women, it is true, experience the peak of sexual desire during the menstrual period. There seems to be sufficient evidence, however, that for a lot of women this is indeed the case, despite the persistent observation in medical literature that women find intercourse during the menses objectionable. It is noteworthy that, perhaps as a consequence of the much-ballyhooed sexual revolution, women's stated attitudes are changing. A 1938 study found that only 2 percent of women polled claimed to enjoy menstrual intercourse.[18] By 1969, 75 percent of Georgia medical students responding to a questionnaire had occasional intercourse during menstruation; another study conducted around the same time by Masters and Johnson revealed that 90 percent of 331 women said they had no objection to this activity as long as they were not at the peak of their flow and their partner expressed no aversion to it.[19] These terms *no objection* and *aversion* bring us to the currently fashionable aesthetic argument against menstrual intercourse.

MENSTRUAL AESTHETIC

The most commonly given reason for avoidance of menstrual intercourse, even among "liberated" men and women, is the couple's aesthetic sensibilities. Seldom do we hear today of the man's disinclination or dread. The word *aesthetic* seems to be a way for male doctors and sociologists to disguise what they really mean: that intercourse with a menstruating woman is messy, sloppy, and possibly frightening; it is also a subtle reinforcement of the message that woman is the "unclean" sex.

WOMAN'S WAY OUT

If a woman does not wish to engage in sexual intercourse, her period is her one legitimate out. Among swingers, this is the only allowable excuse; it is swinger etiquette to plan parties around the female participants' periods. It is also an out for single women. Using "the curse" as an excuse, many a woman has enjoyed a dinner date free from the bothersome knowledge that she herself might be the dessert. Katharina Dalton notes in this regard that some women actually develop prolonged menstruation as a way to avoid sex.[20]

But the menstruation excuse is not merely a modern device. Unterman tells of the Jewish woman who was taken by the Romans and sold into a "house of shame." "She repelled all those who sought to lay lustful hands on her with one cry: 'I am experiencing my menstrual period!' with the result that none molested her." [21]

Among the Tswana of the Beuchanaland, the intercourse taboo is so strong that "many a girl has been able, temporarily at least, to escape the attention of an ardent unwelcome lover by pleading her monthly illness as an excuse." [22]

EXCEPTIONS TO THE RULE

Occasionally, however, one meets an unusual kind of man, a person who, instead of being put off by menstruation, is aroused by it. *Tits & Clits*, a West Coast "comic" book, did a piece on menstruation, really the first attempt of its kind to expose publicly the earthy, uninhibited things women think about the gurgling aesthetics of the menstrual flow. The result is bizarre and funny and consciousness raising in the extreme.[23] One male reader was so excited by what he read that he wrote to the editors and shared his sexual fantasies with them. He spoke of himself as "the Kotex Kid," described a Danish sex film that featured a menstruating woman, and recounted the various ways he and his girl friend violate the intercourse taboo. He is stimulated when she makes dinner "in a flimsy nite gown and black high heels and a belt and Kotex," and the smell of menstrual blood on a pad or in a Tassaway turns him on for a week.

The Trakese of the Caroline Islands and the Maori of New Zealand also find nothing aesthetically unpleasant about intercourse during menstruation, and the New Guinea Manus "attach a positive value" to it.[24] Among the A-kamba, an East African clan, "married people usually perform coitus when the woman is menstruating, because of the belief that she can be impregnated only at this time." [25] The A-kamba people must have an extraordinarily low birth rate.

Among prostitutes, whose living depends on their being

sexually available at all times, the menstrual intercourse taboo is not generally observed. Gail Sheehy, author of *Hustling*, told us that girls who are controlled by pimps must use birth control pills to eliminate the flow altogether because "the show must go on six days a week, every week of the month." Constant use of the pills, of course, will ultimately have a devastating effect on their health. Some prostitutes stuff themselves with cotton; others service their customers orally or manually. Call girls can make their own rules, as can "house" girls under the control of a madam. "Yet, since they cater to all tastes, some of their clients (johns) may *prefer* intercourse during their periods."

Karen Paige has discovered that the intercourse taboo is not consistently observed among Protestants. The women whom Paige interviewed included fifty-six Protestants, eighteen Catholics, and thirteen Jews. Most of the Catholics and Jews said that they "would never have sex during menstruation," but only half the Protestants so responded.[26] In the only study we could find on blacks, statistics indicate that they are *not* exceptions to the rule. In an exploration of the attitudes of over 100 "medically indigent women" in Georgia, all but 3 of whom were black, the intramenstrual taboo was overwhelmingly observed. The women said that menstrual intercourse was "unclean and not right," "undignified," and "not polite." The 3 women in this group who did enjoy sex during menstruation said they did so because they were free from worry about pregnancy.[27]

Despite these exceptions, the rule remains. The intramenstrual taboo is widespread and affects people from all classes and all cultures. One California study shows that of 960 families, "half of the men and women had never had sex during menstruation." [28] Perhaps the vast majority of human beings are just being faithful to their animal ancestry; during the menstrual cycle of female apes, one authority claims, the males "scrupulously avoid serious copulation." The male may mount the female, but he does not try to penetrate. The mounting is no more than a friendly gesture.[29]

Among human beings, it is often difficult for women to ask a sexual partner, especially a new one, "What's wrong with a little blood?" The husband of one woman we talked to, who is sexually experimental in every other respect, prefers to avoid intercourse during her period. So she uses sheets with a red floral pattern. Except for the first day, when the flow is heavy, he doesn't seem to notice that she is menstruating.

Another friend wrote to us about the most extreme case of noncommunication in this area we've heard. A woman who didn't want to alienate her husband during her period had a voluntary hysterectomy:

> She is evidently pleased . . . the operation is accomplished . . . no more birth control . . . no, there was nothing *wrong* with her organs . . . simply quietly she explains that she chose *this* method of birth control so that she won't have to say no to her husband at *that* time . . . about the number 28 they see eye to eye . . . no honey not tonight . . . it's *that* time. . . .

"No honey, not tonight: it's *that* time." The majority of men and women still believe in the inviolability of this taboo, building menstrual huts of fear and superstition wherever and whenever they live.

. . . .

Chapter 3

PUTTING HER IN HER PLACE: RITES OF THE MENARCHE

One of the reasons taboos die so hard—in all types of civiliza-tions—is that they are rigorously taught to youngsters, who dare not question them. To the uninitiated, they represent the status and privilege of adulthood. The concentration with which today's prepubescent girl ponders the menstrual man-uals supplied by the napkin manufacturers and probes the mysteries of the tampon box is only a pale vestige of the rituals observed throughout history and earlier to mark the onset of menstruation.

In most native cultures the world over, the first period is accompanied by rites which give formal notice to the men-archeal child that woman's place in society is indeed a special one. The most widespread practice is the seclusion of the menstruating girl from the tribe for periods lasting from a few days to a few years. During this seclusion, the girl is taboo. She may be prohibited from seeing the sun or touching the ground; she may not feed herself, handle food, or eat certain foods considered dangerous to her in this state. The circle of bushes or whatever barrier is placed between her and her people will probably also serve as her isolation hut during later periods. At the end of her seclusion, the girl is considered marriageable.

Among the more extreme devotees of this practice were the Carrier Indians of British Columbia, who caused a girl to live in the wilderness in complete seclusion for three or four years, far from all the beaten trails, believing that even her footsteps would defile a path.[1] Natives of New Ireland kept their girls at home for the same period of time, but in cages, where they would get fat and pale, in accordance with the tribe's standard of beauty. The richer or more powerful the father, the longer the girl was likely to remain caged; the poor could not afford to lose the labor of their daughters for such a long period.[2] Mohave Indian rites involved the first four menstrual periods,[3] and the Kolosh Indians of Alaska confined pubescent girls in a tiny hut, completely blocked except for one small airhole, for one year, during which time they were allowed no fire, no exercise, no company.[4]

In Cambodia, some girls were put to bed under a mosquito curtain for 100 days. Other Cambodian maidens were said to have "entered into the shade" and were required to observe strict seclusion for up to three years, during which time they would have to observe the traditional prohibitions against seeing the sun (with time out during eclipses).[5] Throughout India, girls became untouchable at puberty and were also forbidden to see the sun during their four-day seclusion.[6] Some Australian tribes were inclined to bury their girls in the sand,[7] as did the Mohave Indians of North America.[8] The Indians of British New Guinea, Brazil, and Bolivia swung their daughters in hammocks for the duration of the menarche.[9]

Sir James Frazer has interpreted such practices to mean that the society believed the newly menstruating girl to be in such danger from the magical powers of the menstrual flow and consequently so great a danger to the society at large that the safest place for her was in a state of suspension between heaven and earth. (Even those girls who were buried in sand observed ceremonial distance from the earth by means of special wraps or shoes.) He noted that this seclusion and suspension are the same for girls at menarche and sacred priests and kings. Both are *sacra;* both are charged with powers so precious to the entire society, that they must be carefully guarded from harm. The seclusion and suspension are for their own protection as well as for the protection of the society, so that there will be no tampering with the divine power in them.[10]

The common association of the sun with "father" may also contribute to the reasons for seclusion of girls at menarche. Torres Strait maidens were enjoined from contact with men, especially their own fathers. This was for their mutual protection. The girl was believed to be in danger of sexual assault by her father, but the father was also facing the same dangers that would befall any man in contact with a menstruating woman: loss of his masculine powers.

At the same time, the father was experiencing a new status in the community. His role in the rites and doctrines of the menarche, suggests Karen Paige, might have come from the economic advantage and bargaining power of a marriageable (barterable) daughter.[11]

Yet another important function of the menarcheal seclusion is its suggestion of time "in the womb" as the girl prepares for her rebirth as a fully functioning member of the society. The strict taboos during seclusion might be necessary because the initiate is in a "marginal" condition (between her ritual death and ritual rebirth) and, like a child in a womb, cannot help or protect herself from raging supernatural influences.[12] Among the societies that emphasize the rebirth symbolism in their rituals are the Navaho and Mohave nations. Both Navaho and Mohave girls are believed to be physically and spiritually malleable during their seclusion. Their female attendants actually massage their backs, arms, and legs, as women of those cultures do with newborn infants, so that they will grow strong and straight. The instructions the girls receive during their seclusion are designed to shape their minds so that as women they will conform as closely as possible to their cultural ideal.[13]

The rebirth notion is also prevalent in India, where it is compatible with the Hindu belief in reincarnation. Just as a newborn child is believed to be an ancestor reincarnate and is given the ancestor's name, so do some initiates receive a new name at puberty. This emphasizes the seriousness of the rebirth symbolism in initiation rites. A highlight of the puberty rite in parts of India is often a magical representation of the act of dying and being born again from the womb. Some candidates for initiation are mourned by their mothers as dead and behave like infants when they return from their seclusion.[14]

Because the appearance of the menses signals that a girl is ready for a productive marriage, many societies use the occasion of the menarche for a ritual defloration, either actual or symbolic. This practice stems from the idea that the menarche is itself a defloration; often, no distinction was made between menstrual and hymenal blood in the primitive mind. It was also employed as a deterrent to the magical spirits and creatures who were especially apt to be hovering around the girl at this time and likely to have intercourse with her.

In Thailand and among certain African societies, it was believed that a girl's first menstruation is a result of her defloration by one of a host of aerial spirits, with each subsequent menstruation caused by further intercourse with these spirits. Thus, at her menarche, a girl was often referred to as a "bride." [15] A similar belief prevails in parts of India. There, ritual defloration or marriage takes place before puberty so that the girl is not placed in the danger of having her first intercourse with a supernatural spirit. This defloration is often performed by a priest, a member of a higher caste, or perhaps a foreigner. Because it is considered dangerous for ordinary members of the society to have intercourse with a menstruating woman, being the cause of the menstruation would be even more dangerous. Frequently, a symbolic defloration satisfied the requirements. The Nayar peoples' menarche rites featured a ceremonial "husband" who tied a small gold plate shaped like a fig leaf around the neck of the prepubescent girl and was paid for his services.[16] And in South Africa, parents of a newly menstruating girl in the A-Kamba tribe are bound to cohabit, either actually or symbolically (husband jumps over wife). It is believed that this practice is a relic of an older ceremonial defloration of the daughter, with her mother fulfilling her role instead [17] (This is one of the few instances where a mother takes an active part in her daughter's ceremonies.)

As if the uncontrollable magic of the spirit world were not enough, a newly menstruating girl was, in many societies, considered to be in special danger from snakes. In the Australian myth of the Wawilak women, the stimulus of menstrual blood is so powerful that the "great snake" is impelled to symbolic intercourse with the women of the myth.[18] Another Australian tribe warns a girl against eating anything that lives in salt water, lest she be killed by a snake.[19] And Mohave Indian girls, during the ritual cleansing of the vulva after the first menstruation, are not to let any water enter the vagina so that they are not overcome by a dread disease caused by "supernatural snakes." [20] The common association of snake and penis indicates that the taboos relating to snakes are another expression of primitive belief that the menarche is the result of a magical defloration. Eve herself gained carnal knowledge and lost her innocence to just such a creature.

Fear of women's blood is, again, at the root of these various fantastic notions about the evils of intercourse with menarcheal girls. Much has been written about the psychological impact of a bloody penis; intercourse with a girl who is experiencing her first menstruation confronts a man with the added onus of the unknown and is therefore doubly dangerous. These feelings are probably at the root of the ambivalent reverence for virginity in most societies.

Even when the distinction between menstrual and hymenal blood is realized, their association in the male unconscious continues. Simone de Beauvoir writes in *The Second Sex:*

> According to whether a man feels himself overwhelmed by the encircling forces or proudly believes himself capable of taking control of them, he declines or demands to have his wife delivered to him a virgin. In the most primitive societies, where women's power is great, it is fear that rules him; it is proper for the woman to be deflorated before the wedding night.[21]

Thus, we find that in societies which consider defloration especially repellent, a surrogate, usually an elder or a midwife, makes the passage for the husband. Although the Catholic church places an extremely high value on virginity and believes that consecrated adult virginity is a superior vocation to marriage, Tertullian, an early church father, writes: "No one is a 'virgin' from the time when she is capable of marriage; seeing that, in her, age has by that time been wedded to its own husband, that is, to time." [22] Tertullian apparently believes, with all primitive peoples in all times, that menarche and deflowering are inextricably linked. The blood itself is the problem, not its fountain of origin.

Symbolically linked with ritual defloration at puberty are all those aspects of the initiation ceremonies that involve pain, mutilation, or modification of the girl's body. Like defloration, bodily modification represents still another attempt by the society to control the dangerous emanations from the menarcheal girl for her own good and for the safety of the society. They are also in many instances designed to prepare the girl for marriage by enhancing her docility, fidelity, or sexual attractiveness.

Common practices among aboriginal peoples of South America are incisions, stinging with ants, beatings—all carried out as a form of "purification," to expel those malignant influences brought about by the menarche.[23] In Australia, certain tribes "smoke" the girls like hams, then rub their bodies with opossum fat and ground charcoal.[24] But the Uaupes of Brazil really go to peculiar lengths to ready their daughters for the responsibilities of marriage. At her menarche, a girl is confined to her house for a month, with only a little bread and water for nourishment. When her seclusion is complete, she is brought out naked to be beaten with sticks by her relatives and friends of her parents until she falls senseless or dead. Hutton Webster notes:

> If she recovers, the flagellation is repeated four times, at intervals of six hours, and it is considered an offense to the parents not to strike hard. Finally the sticks are dipped into pots of meat and fat and given the girl to lick. She is now considered to be a marriageable woman.[25]

The strongly patriarchal Semitic (Arab) tribes of the Middle East used the menarche as the occasion to remove the girl's clitoris or sew up the lips of the vulva to reduce her sexual pleasure and reinforce her need to be dependent on one man. And then there are the Peruvian Iquito, who perform excision of the clitoris and labia at the ages of nine and ten, respectively, "in the presence of men in full war regalia: feathers, paint, and spears." [26] The Bambara tribes also excise the clitoris "to allow the wanzo, the dangerous sexual principle which comes from the female spirit, to drip out with the blood lost by the operation." [27]

Bruno Bettelheim sees these practices as a sign of men's "aggressive emnity," a hostile expression of their fear of women's blood and sexuality. He distinguishes between clitoridectomy (removal of the clitoris) and infibulation (sewing up the entrance to the vagina), acts generally performed by men, and the manipulation of the female genitals that many societies apparently encourage in their girls. He notes that among the Baganda and the Shaheli of Africa, girls are taught by older women to enlarge their labia even before they reach puberty; in Dahomey, pubescent girls are given instruction in massaging the vagina to cause thickening and muscular development of the lips.[28] Such practices are designed to increase the woman's as well as the man's sexual pleasure.

Tattooing is another form of body modification practiced throughout the world in connection with both male and female rites of puberty. There are reports of societies in Paraguay and Brazil in which a girl at her menarche was gouged on the back, breasts, and stomach with a sharp fish or animal tooth and then had ashes rubbed in the wounds for a permanent tatoo.[29] Because the purpose of tattooing is usually sexual attractiveness, it is considered part of a puberty rite. Similarly, ear piercing, a universal custom, has, in India, a sexual function: The hole in the ear is supposed to have a sympathetic effect on opening the womb for easier childbirth.[30] Nor is the length of an adolescent's hair a recently developed symbol of passage. In some primitive cultures, it was the custom to cut a girl's hair at her menarche and continue her seclusion until the hair had grown below her ears.

Not all aboriginal societies inflict such painful reminders of the menarche on their daughters. Contrasted with the cruelty of some South American natives is the beauty of the Navaho ceremony of *Kinaaldá*, the most important of all their religious rites. This menarcheal celebration finds its origin in Navaho mythology; its purpose is to make sex relations holy and effective, and to produce children to carry on the work of the tribe. Features of *Kinaaldá* include seclusion, instruction of the girl in the taboos she must observe as a menstruating woman, and a large tribal celebration when the seclusion and instruction are complete. A girl may undergo *Kinaaldá* more than once during the first year she is menstruating.[31] This ceremony continues today, with modifications.

In India, with its thousands of ethnic groups, the menarche is universally a time for rejoicing, even though the customs of the different peoples continue to involve seclusion, taboo, and the prohibition against seeing the sun or touching the ground. High and low castes observe similar rites. Among the Deshast Brahmins, for example, the first menstruation is a time for seclusion; but at the completion of the seclusion, the girl, seated on a little throne, is visited by neighbors and relatives, given presents, and washed in ceremonial oil. Similarly, a Nayar girl of India will be visited by neighbor women at the end of the seclusion and dressed in new garments, usually the womanly sari, instead of the short dresses she wore as a child. Later, the menstruating girl and her friends undergo a ceremonial bath, followed by a great feast, where "drums are beaten and shouts of joy are given." [32] Among the Manus of the South Pacific (who believe that menstruation is caused by intercourse and therefore conceal each menstruation between the menarche and marriage), the ceremonies of the menarche involve large exchanges of food, splash parties in the lagoons, good times among the women, and the exclusion of men.[33]

Anthropologists continue to question the origins of female initiation rites. The prevailing view is that, like the taboos against the menstruating woman, the rites are devised and perpetrated by men on women; for in no known society have women ever achieved positions of power significant enough to place them in control of these (or any other) vitally important religious ceremonies. Although there have been attempts, as early as the 1870s and as late as the 1970s, to prove that once, in a golden age, women ruled a peaceful world, there is no real evidence that such a society ever existed and, according to a group of feminist anthropologists, "a good deal of evidence to indicate that it did not." [34]

It has also been commonly believed that girls' puberty

rites, being a function of the lesser sex, have been designed to imitate and complement the initiation rites for boys, which have intrigued social observers for decades. Unlike girls' rites, which are individual, boys' rites tend to be conducted in groups. This may be attributable to the absence of a single dramatic sign of puberty in the male, or it may be another way of teaching the children what society expects of them. Boys must endure the pains of circumcision and other ordeals in front of their peers; competition to endure the trials more stoically than the other boys thus becomes an important aspect of the ceremony. Girls, meanwhile, are being instructed by their older relatives—and by the very nature of their ceremonies—in the virtues of passivity. In this sense, the rites do complement each other. But it is unlikely that the girls' rites were developed as an afterthought; there is, rather, internal evidence showing that the boys' rites are designed to imitate menstruation (see Chapter 26).

One anthropologist, Judith Brown, made a cross-cultural study in 1961 of menarche rites and their relation to the position of women in a society. She found that girls' puberty rites occurred most frequently in those societies that observed matrilocal residence (the husband moves in with the wife's family). Such rites are more honorific and less painful than many we have described here. Brown finds instead that the painful rites are related to conditions of child rearing that foster a conflict in sex identity:

> Painful female initiation rites are also related to male initiation rites characterized by both a genital operation and seclusion. Since male rites are also strongly related to the presence of a conflict in sex identity, perhaps the latter condition makes it necessary for society to force both sexes to accept their respective roles.[35]

Although her theory has been both attacked and defended by others in her field, Brown seems to be one of the first anthropologists to seek an explanation for girls' puberty rites that does not equate them with the inferior position of women in most societies.

Chapter 4

WOMAN UNCLEAN: MENSTRUAL TABOOS IN JUDAISM AND CHRISTIANITY

Codified, organized discrimination against menstruating women in the Jewish and Christian cultures begins in Genesis. God tells Eve he will "multiply thy sorrow and thy conception" (3:16). The Book of the prophet Micah refers more directly to menstrual pain: "Be in pain, and labour to bring forth, O daughter of Zion, like a woman in travail" (4:10). To biblical authors, the process was not only painful but also taboo. In a later chapter of Genesis, Rachel keeps her father's household gods from him by claiming she is menstruating. Sitting on the camel's saddle where she has hidden the stolen images, Rachel tells her father, "Let it not displease my lord that I cannot rise before thee; for the custom of women is upon me" (31:35).

A menstrual rag is used as an image of something loathsome to be discarded; in the Book of the prophet Isaiah, "Ye shall defile also the covering of thy graven images of silver, and the ornament of thy molten images of gold; thou shalt cast them away as a menstruous cloth; thou shalt say unto it, Get thee hence" (30:22).

The words of Leviticus 15:19–33 speak most clearly of the

horrors of menstruating women and what they must do to erase the stain:

And if a woman have an issue, and her issue in her flesh be blood, she shall be put apart seven days: and whosoever toucheth her shall be unclean until the even.

And every thing that she lieth upon in her separation shall be unclean: every thing also that she sitteth upon shall be unclean.

And whosoever toucheth her bed shall wash his clothes, and bathe himself in water, and be unclean until the even.

And whosoever toucheth any thing that she sat upon shall wash his clothes, and bathe himself in water, and be unclean until the even.

And if it be on her bed, or on any thing whereon she sitteth, when he toucheth it, he shall be unclean until the even.

And if any man lie with her at all, and her flowers be upon him, he shall be unclean seven days; and all the bed whereon he lieth shall be unclean.

And if a woman have an issue of her blood many days out of the time of her separation, or if it run beyond the time of her separation; all the days of the issue of her uncleanness shall be as the days of her separation: she shall be unclean.

Every bed whereon she lieth all the days of her issue shall be unto her as the bed of her separation: and whatsoever she sitteth upon shall be unclean, as the uncleanness of her separation.

And whosoever toucheth those things shall be unclean, and shall wash his clothes, and bathe himself in water, and be unclean until the even.

But if she be cleansed of her issue, then she shall number to herself seven days, and after that she shall be clean.

And on the eighth day she shall take unto her two turtles or two young pigeons, and bring them unto the priest, to the door of the tabernacle of the congregation.

And the priest shall offer the one for a sin offering, and the other for a burnt offering; and the priest shall make an atonement for her before the Lord for the issue of her uncleanness.

Thus shall ye separate the children of Israel from their uncleanness; that they die not in their uncleanness, when they defile my tabernacle that is among them.

This is the law of him that hath an issue, and of him whose seed goeth from him, and is defiled therewith;

And of her that is sick of her flowers, and of him that hath an issue, of the man, and of the woman, and of him that lieth with her that is unclean.

The position of women in all of the books of the Bible, both Old and New Testaments, depends upon these rules in Leviticus. The fact of menstruation kept women out of the temples and out of the political and economic life of their times. A biblical heroine like Queen Esther could say proudly, "Thou knowest that I abhor the sign of my high estate [her crown] . . . as a menstruous rag" (Esther 14:16).

Obviously, the practices of the ancient Hebrews parallel the taboos and practices of many of the other early societies we have mentioned. The difference is that Judaism has never abolished the taboos; even today, an Orthodox Jewish woman is required to abstain from sex until seven days after her period has ended and after she has immersed herself in the *mikveh*, or ritual bath. There is an interesting defense of this practice in the July 1974 *Ms.*, written by Bracha Sacks, who calls herself both an Orthodox Jew and a feminist: "We do this because God commanded it. One thing is certain though: We are NOT unclean. . . . The woman is not kept out of the synagogue, nor is she forbidden to carry out most of her activities. Only the sexual relationship is forbidden." In speaking of the mikveh, she says, "The purpose of the ritual is completely spiritual . . . it hasn't anything to do with physical cleanliness, as we bathe and shower first. If menstrual blood suggests the death of the potential fetus, the *Mikveh* waters suggest a life-giving element." [1]

Christianity did little to improve the status of women, although Jesus himself was said to be far more enlightened than his successors. In an episode related in John 4:1–42, Jesus is traveling through Samaria on his way to Galilee and asks a woman drawing water at a well to let him drink from her vessel: "Then saith the woman of Samaria unto him, How is it that thou, being a Jew, askest drink of me, which am a woman of Samaria?" (4:9). Jesus then instructs her in the "living water" he will offer and convinces her that he is the Messiah.

Customarily interpreted in the light of political hostilities between the Jews and the Samaritans, this story takes on a new meaning when one is aware of the Rabbinic regulation that, from the viewpoint of Leviticus, the Samaritan women are, from birth, considered as unclean as menstruating women. Thus, Jesus, in asking to share the same drinking cup with this woman who was both religiously and politically anathema to his people, was flagrantly violating the laws of his nation. The surprise of the apostles and the woman's friends attests to the bizarre nature of his actions. A contemporary writer about women and Catholicism uses this incident to show that Jesus "repudiates centuries of thought and legislation which would define woman in her *specific mature womanliness* [italics ours] as unclean and unfit for direct association not only with the divine, but even periodically with the human." [2]

Jesus' best-known encounter with the menstrual taboo is the miracle he performed on the woman with the "issue of blood." This poor soul had been bleeding from the genitals for twelve years. Aware that she was thus ritually unclean, she dared not approach Jesus directly but came up behind him and touched the hem of his robe. Immediately, she was cured, Jesus saying to her, "Thy faith hath made thee whole" (Matthew 9:20–22, Mark 5:25–34, Luke 8:43–48). Here, as at the well, Jesus was using the most elementary and important aspect of the purification laws to demonstrate the new spiritual purification he preached. [3]

But those who made Christianity a worldwide religion listened less to Jesus than to the urgings of their own cultural predilections. Instances of the continuing viability of the laws in Leviticus spot the history of Christianity from the earliest centuries to the present. Even a 1953 edition of *The Interpreter's Bible* takes note of the relative invalidity of the purification laws in the modern world with the comment that "a sense of *natural disgust or shame* [italics ours] has been developed into an ethical and religious feeling of uncleanness." [4]

Of special concern to the church fathers of the first millennium was the question: Should a menstruating woman enter a church or receive communion? In an incident related in the Venerable Bede's *History of the English Church and People,* Augustine, bishop of Canterbury, sent a series of doctrinal questions to Pope Gregory I. Among them were the following: May a woman properly enter church at certain periods? And may she receive communion at these times? Gregory's reply was yes: "The monthly courses of women are not their fault because nature causes them." [5]

By 1963, however, a shade of remonstrance colored the reply. The *Handbook of Moral Theology,* intended for men in Ireland studying for the priesthood, has this to add to the echoes of Leviticus: "Involuntary pollution and the menstrual period do not render the body so unclean as to prevent the receiving of Holy Communion when there exists a right reason for approaching the sacrament." [6] And in 1970, the Levitical injunctions were among the arguments used to justify an American Roman Catholic prohibition against women serving in the sanctuary as lectors and commentators during Mass.[7]

Not even the Mother of God was spared. Popular tradition recalls that when Mary reached puberty, "There was held a council of the priests, saying, 'Behold, Mary has reached the age of twelve years in the temple of the Lord. What shall we do with her, lest perchance she defile the sanctuary of the Lord?' " [8] The reference is to the expected appearance of the menses in Mary and the sacrilegious possibility that she might be present in the temple, where she had been raised and educated since birth, when the menarche occurred. The answer was to betroth her to Joseph and get her out of the holy place. This interesting bit of fancy put Mary in the same position as the scores of girls whose societies believed the menarche to be a defloration by aerial spirits or who were ritually deflowered by human agents at that time. The immediate birth of Jesus suggests another primitive belief, that the firstborn of a young woman was the strongest of all children because it was formed from menstrual blood at its most powerful—right after the menarche.

So, throughout its formative years, during the development of the great intellectual and doctrinal systems, Christianity clung to the Old Testament belief in the uncleanness of woman and the basically imperfect nature that was a consequence of the menstrual flow. Menstruation was even involved in one of the many heresies that plagued the early church, this one perpetrated by one Bishop Valentinus. In an elaborate scheme involving numerology as well as ancient Middle Eastern religions, the "woman with issue" of the Gospels was seen as a precursor of a spirit named Sophia (wisdom), who attempted a direct relationship with the source of all knowledge, sidestepping the wisdom of her brother spirits. Sophia failed in her quest, however, and brought forth an amorphous substance "such as her female nature enabled her to produce." When she saw it, it is reported, her reaction was "one of grief, on account of the imperfection of its generation." [9] Sophia's emanation (menstrual blood) is an example of the Aristotelian belief that menstrual blood was the *matter* of creation, to which the sperm gave *form*. As a menstruating woman, Sophia could not hope to produce knowledge because knowledge was formal and hence masculine. Aristotle's theories of the matter and form of creation kept a tenacious hold on Christian doctrine for centuries thanks to Thomas Aquinas and his codification of the Aristotelian tenets. He described woman as a "misbegotten male":

> As regards the individual nature, woman is defective and misbegotten for the active power in the male seed tends to the production of a perfect likeness according to the masculine sex; while the production of woman comes from defect in the active power or from some material indisposition, or even from some external influence, such as that of a south wind, which is moist.[10]

The inferiority of women is once again explained as being a result of her menstrual flow, believed to be the passive, "moist," therefore imperfect agent in procreation.

Christianity played a large part in the perpetration of yet another crime against women: the witch-hunts of medieval Europe and colonial America. During the terror known as the Inquisition, the vast majority of the hundreds of thousands of persons put to death for "heresy" were women, women who were accused of being witches on the same evidence that men since the dawn of human life had been using to taboo and isolate the menstruating woman.

Pliny's list of the disastrous effects of menstruating women on men, cows, gardens, bees, milk, wine could be a catalog of the evil effects of witchcraft as it was understood by church and state in Europe. The infamous *Malleus maleficarum* ("hammer of witches") comes down to us today as the handbook of witch-hunting and provides a documented link between the church's attitudes toward women's bodies and their persecution of the witches. The *Malleus* urged Inquisitors to look to a woman when witchcraft was suspected in a neighborhood "because she is more carnal than man as is clear from her many carnal abominations." [11] For "carnal abominations," read "menstrual blood." The *Malleus* itself was inspired by the famous 1488 Bull of Pope Innocent VIII, which, in its list of the horrors of witches, reads like Pliny on the evils of menstruating women:

> [Witches] have slain infants yet in the mother's womb, as also the offspring of cattle, have blasted the produce of the earth, the grapes of the vine, the fruits of trees, nay men and women, beasts of burthen, herd-beasts, as well as animals of other kinds, vineyards, orchards, meadows, pastureland, corn, wheat and all other cereals; these wretches furthermore afflict and torment men and women, beasts of burthen, herd-beasts, as well as animals of other kinds, with terrible and piteous pains and sore diseases, both internal and external; they hinder men from performing the sexual act and women from conceiving, whence husbands cannot know their wives nor wives receive their husbands. [12]

In many respects, organized religion is still in the Middle Ages when it comes to women. But there are indications that at least some of the faithful are exploring the old taboos in a new and exciting way.

In his 1973 play *The Prodigal Daughter*, set in a Catholic rectory in England and centering on the young housekeeper who is repenting an abortion, David Turner introduces the concept of an androgynous Jesus. The youngest of three priests in the rectory is disturbed by the church's indifference to the plight of women such as the heroine and an unseen old nun who is dying of cancer of the womb, cursing God. The young priest cries out in anguish that Christ must have been a woman. God incarnate could not have denied to itself the full experience of humanity; it could not have refused to partake in woman's nature, "in her gestations, her menstruations, her orgasms." Twenty centuries of Christianity have only now brought us to this concept. For if God menstruates, then menstruation becomes godly. If menstruation is godly, then woman has at least a chance of becoming godly herself. [13]

. . . .

Chapter 5

MENSTRUATION AND MEDICAL MYTH

When we move from myth to medicine, we see that even the scientific explanations for menstruation have been colored by the same fear and wonder of the most primitive peoples on earth. By the late nineteenth century—when political and social revolutions had irrevocably altered the course of world affairs and *The Origin of the Species* had successfully and finally challenged man's solipsistic view of his universal worth—menstruation was still a mystery to men.

We can hardly be surprised that menstruation remained a medical mystery for so long.. Those studying it—men—didn't menstruate, and as these men of science pursued their objective explorations into the female reproductive system, few (if any) thought to ask a woman for basic facts and figures about the monthly cycle. The weird theories put forth in the advancement of menstrual knowledge reveal at least as much about the men as they do about the menses.

NUTRITIVE THEORY

Aristotle was one of the earliest to tackle the problem: he saw menstruation as a sign of female inferiority, related to the passive part he felt women played in reproduction. Aristotle's *On the Generation of Animals* was enormously influential and became the standard treatise on embryology from the fourth century B.C. until William Harvey's work on embryology in the seventeenth century A.D.

In *On the Generation of Animals,* Aristotle explains the contribution of male and female to the production of a child: "The female always provides the material, the male provides that which fashions the material into shape; this, in our view, is the specific characteristic of each of the sexes: that is what it means to be male or to be female." [1] The male, then, is the active partner; the female is passive.

Aristotle adds that "the physical part, the body comes from the female, and the Soul comes from the male, since the Soul is the essence of a particular body" (2. 4. 185). Again, the male performs the more valued part. Lest one see the sexes as complementary in creating a child, Aristotle makes it clear that they are not: "We should look upon the female state as being as it were a deformity, though one which occurs in the ordinary course of nature" (4. 6. 461). (This is the source of the sexual theology of Thomas Aquinas discussed in Chapter 4.)

The outward sign of female inferiority is menstruation. The female is deficient, says Aristotle, in performing the task of "concoction." (The Greek word for concoction, *pepsis,* is the same word used for ripening or maturing fruit or corn with heat.) Because the female does not have enough natural vital heat, her concocting achievement proceeds only as far as menstrual blood. This forms the embryo's "Nutritive Soul." The male, however, can transform matter with heat and produce semen, the end product of concoction. The colder female, in other words, is a case of arrested development. She cannot go beyond menstrual blood to produce semen.

Hence, says Aristotle, a residue of useless nourishment gathers in her blood vessels (in fact, menstrual bleeding is from the capillaries in the uterine lining, not from major blood vessels). When the blood vessels are full, an overflow is necessary; this overflow is menstruation (4. 5. 451).

Later writers did not question Aristotle's beliefs. Menstrual blood was the passive female matter; semen was the outward sign of the active male principle. The Roman historian Pliny, for instance, concluded in the first century A.D. that women who do not menstruate "are incapable of bearing children because it is of this substance that the infant is formed. The seed of the male, acting as a sort of leaven, causes it to unite and assume a form, and in due time it acquires life and assumes a bodily shape." [2]

Seventeen hundred years later, the French naturalist Georges de Buffon agreed with Aristotle on the supremacy of the male role: "The male semen is the sculptor, the menstrual blood is the block of marble, and the fetus is the figure which is fashioned out of the combination." [3]

Aristotle's theory had stated, in effect, that the menses is a substance intended to nourish the fetus. Because believers in this nutritive theory were ignorant of or uncertain about the ovum's existence (until the nineteenth century), they assumed that the nutritive substance was the only female contribution to reproduction.

PLETHORA THEORY

Another popular theory suggests that women have an over-abundance, that they have more of something than men do, not less. But the standard of health is still a male one from which women may deviate in either direction.

According to this theory, women have a unique need for "evacuation." This need is explained in several different ways. Pythagoras (sixth century B.C.) saw the menses as eliminating extra blood. According to Empedocles, a century later, this need for evacuation stemmed from the different densities of flesh; the male flesh, denser, has no need for evacuation. Parmenides, also in the fifth century B.C., stated (in opposition to Aristotle) that woman is "hotter" than man and therefore contains more blood, of which she eliminates a part each month. Through the course of her life, she becomes progressively "colder" until she reaches menopause.[4]

Galen (second century A.D.) saw in menstruation an evacuation of the fluids or juices women accumulated in an idle life: "I imagine that the female sex, inasmuch as they heap up a great quantity of humours, by living continually at home, and not being used to hard labour, or exposed to the sun, should receive a discharge of this fullness, as a remedy given by nature." [5] Even today, there are those who, like Galen, seem to believe that woman's work, housework, is not hard work.

Soranus, in the same era as Galen, mentions the popular belief that the menses get rid of surplus matter in women in the same way that men eliminate it in athletics.[6] That belief, unlike the others, sees the sexes as complementary; the female is not a deviation from the norm. But for the most part, a certain denigration of women is suggested in both the nutritive theory and the plethora theory.

FERMENT THEORY

Avicenna, the eleventh-century Arab physician, agreed that menstruation was caused by an overabundance of blood in women, but he added his impression of the female body. According to Avicenna, menstrual blood is eliminated through the womb because that organ is the weakest and the last formed.[7]

In the seventeenth century, Regnier de Graaf (after whom the ovarian follicle is named) agreed that the uterus is the weak point of the female and hence the outlet for the menses. He also added an analogy to Avicenna's formulation: "The menstrual blood escapes by the feeblest parts of the body, in the same way that wine or beer undergoing fermentation escapes by defective parts of the barrel." [8] This, then, was the concept of menses as ferment (or womb as defective barrel).

John Freind (eighteenth century) attempted to reconcile plethora and ferment. According to Freind, women are more moist and have more blood than men, and this is a reason for their attaining full growth sooner. If a man did have a plethora of blood, Freind says that it would escape, through hemorrhoids or bloody urine. If this discharge were kept inside, however, a "distemper" would ensue, the man might become "hysteric," and he might die.[9]

Freind argued in part against de Graaf's theory of ferment or "vehement effervescence" because the theory did not explain where the ferment was hidden, only its means of escape. Instead, Freind attempted to prove that the plethora exists in women. With mathematical similes, diagrams, and analogies from physics, Freind explained the belief for this plethora through the periodic discharge of blood. He also insisted that the length of menstrual cycles is a multiple of seven: usually fourteen, twenty-one, or twenty-eight days. Freind's work is admirable for its symmetry, but it makes little sense.

STEPHENSON WAVE

The idea that the amount of blood circulates rather freely, yet escapes where it might most easily do so (the womb as weak point) also becomes a part of the "Stephenson wave" explanation for menstruation. Dr. William Stephenson, who described his wave theory in the *American Journal of Obstetrics* in 1882, felt that menstruation is associated with a "wave of vital energy" shown in the body temperature, the daily amount of urine, and the pulse rate. This wave is varied but works in cycles, menstruation coinciding with the average body temperature. When the excessive nutritive material and vital energy are not used in reproduction, they are used in menstruation.[10]

The Stephenson wave theory also explains vicarious menstruation. If there is an obstruction, the wave is thrown to whatever point of the system is weakest. Hence, says G. Stanley Hall after citing Stephenson in his own *Adolescence* (1908), every trouble in woman demands special attention to the pelvis.[11] Hall, like many of his predecessors, seems to adopt the ancient definition of woman: *Tota mulier in utero* ("Woman is a womb").

Most menstrual theorists did glimpse a portion of the truth. The lining of the womb becomes menstrual fluid unless it is needed for an embryo's nutrition, so the nutritive theory is partially vindicated. There is a sort of plethora when conception does not occur, in that the lining is no longer needed. The womb is the convenient place for the escape of this fluid.

But nearly all menstrual theorists also imposed their own order upon their material observations, and their ordering was shaped by patriarchal preconceptions. They reasoned that menstruation was a sign of woman's otherness, hence a sign of her inferiority; their next step was to rationalize this inferiority through whatever science was at their disposal. And that kind of rationalization is hardly dead in our own era.

AGE AT MENARCHE

From the inferiority of all women, the early theorists moved easily to the idea that the age at which a woman first menstruates may be a sign of the inferiority of her ethnic group or an indication that she has been leading a wicked life. The fact is, the age at menarche (first menstruation) depends greatly on good food and good health. Those who eat well mature earlier. Today, the average American girl first menstruates when she is 12½ years old. Figures from Norway, where the oldest such records are kept, show that in 1850 the average girl had her first period at 17; by 1950, at 13½.[12] For each generation since 1850, then, a girl's period has come about a year earlier than her mother's.

The association of the lowering menarcheal date with modern nutritional advances is today a popularly acknowledged "fact." But this statistic, too, may be questionable. Nineteenth-century women, laboring under the old equation—menarche equals first intercourse equals fallen woman—may have given a later date for their first menarche out of modesty or embarrassment.

The earliest researchers gave only impressionistic testimony about age at menarche. Soranus claimed that menstruation first appears in the fourteenth year.[13] The great medieval scientist Albertus Magnus, in the thirteenth century, said that 14 was the most frequent age at menarche.[14] However, the Virgin Mary, according to medieval tradition, was 14 when she conceived. Because the ancient and medieval minds did not always distinguish myth from what we call scientific fact, Albertus's sources of information could be theology rather than observation.

By 1869, the empirical method of data gathering was more generally used, and an enterprising scientist named Krieger classified the age of young women at menarche according to country. In Lapland, for instance, girls bled first at 18; in Germany, at 15 years, 7 months, and 6 days; in Egypt, at 10.[15] Krieger's figures are suspect because he probably depended on the memories of the women he interviewed, but the vast body of such studies, by Krieger and others, reveal a number of cultural prejudices disguised as scientific fact.

Climate was one obsession of the researchers. Although the later and more reliable studies indicate no correlation, scientists as early as 1704 wanted to believe that the hot-blooded wenches near the equator bled first. Richard Mead, one of George II's physicians, wrote in that year that "everyone knows how great a share the moon has in forwarding those evacuations of the weaker sex" and that near the equator the lunar pull toward menses would be the greatest.[16]

Over a century later, August Bebel agreed with the earlier age for tropical women, claiming that warm climates stimulate the sexual drive but that the unfortunate Eskimo girls do not menstruate until age 19.[17] The nineteenth-century American physician Pye Henry Chavasse added that in warm climates, "such as in Abyssinia and India," girls menstruate at 10 or 11 but that in Russia menarche does not occur until 20 to 30 years of age, and even then only three to four times a year.[18] And Eskimos, according to the nineteenth-century doctor George MacDiarmid, menstruate only during the summer months.[19]

Such generalizations seem based less on observations (which often invalidate them) than on cultural assumptions about the relationship of climate and sex, with the menarche, even in scientific terms, a continuing symbol of sexuality. One cultural assumption is an old Anglo-Saxon one: that the darker races are more sensual than the fair. The slave traders, entertaining the prejudices of their own societies, assumed that Africans were more sexually inclined because the latter (sensibly) wore fewer clothes than Europeans. In the European and American minds, the torrid regions were expected to produce early sexual maturity. As late as 1920, it was common belief that early sexual experience and/or early marriage (i.e., an early stimulation of the genitals) would cause an earlier menarche. Studying women of India who married very young, another researcher found the belief was totally false.[20]

Similarly, a 1951 American textbook by K. C. Garrison, *Psychology of Adolescence*, asserts without proof that "colored children in America mature earlier than white children of the same age." [21] C. L. Henton tested this hypothesis and found no significant difference between black and white girls. Again, Garrison's text may have reflected a common cultural preconception: that blacks have more and earlier sexual activity than whites and hence must menstruate earlier.

It is not only with the darker races that the menarche and sexual morality are linked. A similar association about white American girls appears in nineteenth-century texts. Dr. Carpenter, in his *Physiology,* observed that "girls brought up in the midst of luxury or sensual indulgence undergo this change earlier than those reared in poverty and self-denial." [22] The *New Warren's Household Physician* insists that the menarche is "hastened by high living; by the whirl and bustle and excitement of city life; by reading novels which are full of love-incidents; by attending balls, theatres, and parties; and by mingling much in the society of gentlemen." [23] To such writers, the menarche appears to be both a literal and a figurative stain, a sign of a badly ordered existence.

Whether the age at menarche does, indeed, involve either moral turpitude or moral grace is doubtful. Nor does maturity correlate with hair color. One study asserts that blondes menstruate about a year earlier than brunettes. Another argues that redheads are first and have a peculiar smell; still another gives the nod to brunettes.[24]

Weber, who studied Russian women in the nineteenth century, argued for a relationship between profession and periods. He claimed that teachers, singers, actresses, and other women who showed an inclination for the professions menstruated exceptionally early; but again, he is ascribing to women who worked, no doubt because they had to, an attribute commonly linked with immoral behavior.[25]

Strange Case of Pubertas Praecox

Menstruation before age 9 is *precocious puberty.* Extremely early menarche may be caused by tumors or other abnormalities, such as dwarfism or rickets. Most literature on the subject has more the aura of folklore than of medical report. Cases of menstruation at age 7 days, 6 weeks, and 2, 3, and 7 months are among the earliest recorded.[26]

The first precocious case reported by name is Anna Mummenthaler, a patient of G. E. Von Haller (Bern, 1751). She had her menarche at 2, gave birth to a full-term child at 9, reached menopause at 52, and died at 75.[27] Menstruating for nearly fifty years may in itself be a record.

Rather less fortunate was her contemporary Eva Christine Fischer of Eisenach.[28] Born in 1750, she was as developed as a woman of 20 by 1753. She was "exhibited" in the Easter Fair at Leipzig, it is reported, and died not long afterward, in May 1753. Perhaps as a reward for her pains, she is depicted in the Leipzig anatomical school.

In the nineteenth century, *pubertas praecox* took on moral overtones. *Lancet,* the British medical journal, reported a mother under 11 years old, the youngest example the writer was aware of. The writer hoped the age would not be surpassed, "for it manifests a depraved precocity which is truly lamentable in a Christian country." [29] Although a male was surely involved, the girl's early maturity seems to be all that is considered depraved.

In the present century, precocious puberty is more likely to be probed than exhibited or condemned. In Peru, in 1939, Lina Medina, 5½ years old, gave birth to a normal healthy boy. The girl had menstruated from the age of 8 months. Lina was regarded neither as a fallen woman nor as a sideshow candidate, but as a rather unfortunate little girl whose menarche was extremely early.[30]

The age of menarche has long fascinated medical researchers, nearly all of whom were male. The fascination may be with what makes a woman different from a man, but it may also be read as an attempt to control that difference by analyzing and defining it.

. . . .

Chapter 6

MODERN MENSTRUAL POLITICS

It was the last day of the long Senate debate over Joint Resolution 208, otherwise known as the Equal Rights Amendment. The leader of the opposition, the self-proclaimed protector of women from the implications of their equality, took the floor to offer still another set of amendments designed to weaken ERA. As was his custom, Senator Sam Ervin, later to be a hero of Watergate but now little more than an anachronism to the hundreds of women who lined the galleries, cited what he considered to be the ultimate authority for his argument:

> We find in Chapter 1, Verse 27 of the book of Genesis this statement which all of us know to be true: "God created man in his own image. In the image of God created He him. Male and female, created He them. . . ." When He created them, God made physiological and functional differences between men and women. These differences confer upon men a greater capacity to perform arduous and hazardous physical tasks.[1]

Even on March 22, 1972, forty-nine years after the amendment had first been proposed to Congress, one of the most respected U.S. senators was linking the Bible with the old question of equal rights for women. The final vote that day, approving the resolution 84 to 8, reflected the legislators' ability to divorce religion from reality in matters of state. But Senator Sam's use of the Bible (as well as a staggering number of articles in scholarly and legal journals) to prove women do not deserve to have equal protection and responsibilities under law is a perfect illustration of the power of one religious tradition to keep the "physiological and functional" differences between men and women in the forefront of all debate about women's intellectual and professional freedom.

Since the advent of modern science, the fears and prejudices surrounding menstruation have given way to an acceptance of it as a normal bodily process—at least in print. But the habits of centuries are not easily unlearned by men who depend on woman's manifest physical differences to give a rationale for their belief in her emotional, economic, and social otherness. That is why the system we call *menstrual politics* has by no means disappeared with the twentieth century and the "emancipation" of women from their biologically determined roles.

For the sake of argument, in reviewing the last hundred years or so, we are going to leave in the background the multiple movements in U.S. history that produced the drive for full female equality and concentrate instead on the one constant fact about women: their menstruation. The resulting picture puts in sharp focus how far we've come—and how far we have yet to go.

Practitioners of menstrual politics have one basic tenet in common: They are convinced that women are naturally and irrevocably limited by the menstrual function. Since the early nineteenth century, menstrual politics has taken two positions with regard to menstruation and economic life: first, that *factories and businesses pose a fatal threat to women's reproductive life;* second, that *the menstrual cycle threatens the health of American capitalism.* The progression of ideas has been from the first to the second; as medicine began paying more attention to the facts of the menstrual cycle and medical excuses for the exclusion of women waned, the idea that menstruation was bad for business gained in popularity, and that is where we are now. In this second wave of the American woman's movement, at a moment in history when man has so mastered his universe that he is beginning to redefine even life and death, women are still hearing from people like Edgar Berman, a physician and Democratic party functionary, who announced in 1970 that he would not like to see a woman in charge of this country at a time of national crisis because her "raging hormonal imbalances" would threaten the life and safety of all.

But the first phase of American menstrual politics was no less insidious for all its creaky chivalry. On the one hand, it was instrumental in getting some legislative relief for the thousands of women employed in the sweatshops and "dark satanic mills" of the nineteenth century. On the other, the bodily weakness attributed to the menstrual function became a favored argument for restricting the participation of women in higher education and national affairs. A continuing monument to the politics of menstrual exclusion in this country is the body of "protective" legislation that restricts women's working hours, women's duties, and ultimately, women's pay and prestige.

Women had been working in the factories and mills since the industrial revolution. England and New England alike exploited young women and children, working them as much as sixteen hours a day for as little as a dollar a week. Only very gradually did women organize in the nineteenth and twentieth centuries to change these conditions. The fledgling labor movement, then as now, was more concerned with stabilizing conditions for men. Few women had power in the AFL unions; perhaps their Victorian sense of obligation to their paternalistic employers prevented them from getting any real power on their own.[2]

Meanwhile, some states, alarmed at the appalling working conditions endured by *both* sexes, had tried to legislate humane practices. One such law, a New York statute setting maximum hours of work for bakery employees, had been declared unconstitutional by the U.S. Supreme Court in 1905 (*Lochner* v. *New York* 198 U.S. 45). But in 1908, the Court sent down a decision whose implications would have a significant effect on the ratification of ERA. It upheld the constitutionality of an Oregon law that restricted the employment of women in any "mechanical establishment, or factory, or laundry" to ten hours a day. What the Court believed set this law apart from the New York statute was the question of sex:

> That woman's physical structure and the performance of material functions place her at a disadvantage in the struggle for subsistence is obvious. This is especially true when the burdens of motherhood are upon her. *Even when they are not, by abundant testimony of the medical fraternity continuance for a long time on her feet at work, repeating this from day to day, tends to have injurious effects upon the body,* and as healthy mothers are essential to vigorous offspring, the physical well-being of women becomes an object of public interest and care in order to preserve the strength and vigor of the race. (*Muller* v. *Oregon* 202 U.S. 412 [1908]) (italics ours)

Regarded as a stunning victory for women in 1908, and progenitor of many state protective laws, *Muller* v. *Oregon* was still being cited in the U.S. Senate in 1972 as an argument for the defeat of ERA. It made no distinction between pregnant and nonpregnant women and classified all women as mothers or potential mothers. The state's interest in the bodies of all women was established—for the good of the preservation of the race.

Labor-union women and others who fought for the protective laws were principally interested in gaining a minimum standard of working conditions. They believed that minimum standards for women would be merely a first step toward humane conditions for all. But because the Court made its decision on the basis of "woman's physical structure" and the "strength and vigor of the race," the laws that followed the 1908 decision tended to restrict women more than help them; whereas men's hours—and salaries—remained limitless. Laws after *Muller* restricted the number of pounds a woman might lift, the kind of place she might work in, the number of rest breaks she must take during the day.

The debate in the courts was accompanied by strident debate among doctors over the effects on menstruation of living an active life. One controversy threatened to undo the progress of higher education for women, which had also been gaining momentum early in the nineteenth century. In 1874, a small book by one Edward F. Clarke, M.D., proposed that educating women would mean the end of the human race. Titled *Sex in Education,* its thesis was that American girls were generally feebler than their European sisters because of the deplorable trend toward higher education for women. The college years, Clarke believed, followed too soon on the menarche, when the debilitating effects of the newly flowing menstrual blood made the body susceptible to disease and outside influence. Studying forced the brain to use up the blood and energy needed to get the menstrual process functioning efficiently. Allowing young women to continue their studies would thus result in the weakening of women and consequently the weakening of generations of Americans as yet unborn. For of course, woman, to Clarke, was defined by her uterus, as she was to the 1908 Supreme Court: "Let the fact be accepted that there is nothing to be ashamed of in a woman's organization, and let her whole education and life be guided by the divine requirements of her system." [3]

The uproar caused by Clarke's book is a measure of the extent to which thinking people were in favor of the education of women and were willing to answer Clarke in his own language. Several rebuttals were published, among them *Sex and Education,* a collection of essays by distinguished educators and public figures, edited by Julia Ward Howe (author of "The Battle Hymn of the Republic"). Most significant in this volume was the testimony from colleges admitting women, Vassar, Antioch, Michigan, Oberlin among them. Alida C. Avery, Vassar's resident physician, assured Dr. Clarke that students were forbidden to attend gym classes during the first two days of their periods and were denied physical education if they suffered from dysmenorrhea (painful menstruation). But the reports from these institutions all supported the thesis that education and discipline and regular exercise improve menstrual health and general vigor, thus contributing to a healthier and more intelligent population of mothers. [4]

While declaring the halls of ivy off limits to any female person, Clarke had not shown similar concern for the mills, factories, and sweatshops that were the college of thousands of unfortunate young women. Clarke had, in fact, declared that factory work was not so damaging to young girls as studying, for bodily strain did not tax the fragile new menstrual process the way mental exertion did. But in 1875, Dr. Azel Ames, in *Sex in Industry,* spoke of the evil results of "co-ordinated mental and physical activity on the menstrual function." [5] He called for laws that would prevent the exploitation of cheap female labor. Nonetheless, the message of both men was the same: If you let women out of the home and into the man's world, their reproductive lives would be so damaged that the future of the human race would be irrevocably jeopardized.

And so the arguments went. The major theme seemed to be that emancipation of women would mean the destruction of their menstrual cycles and thus the end of the human race, for woman exists to bear children. Even the real need for labor reform could not mask the determination to keep woman "in her place" and to provide a physical basis for doing so, so that competence, skill, strength, or intelligence could have no bearing on her advancement.

The turning point seems to have come around the time women gained the vote; large percentages of the female population were gaining advanced degrees, entering the professions, and in general reaping the benefits of the "century of struggle" for legal and political equality. An enormously liberating factor in these advances was the mass marketing of disposable sanitary napkins after World War I. Before Kotex came on the market in 1921, women had been wearing garments similar to babies' diapers, which they washed and reused. Imagine the effect this cumbersome and unhygienic garment must have had on the average woman's workday outside the home, whether in a factory or in an office, and you have some idea of why women probably did not venture out of the house when they menstruated. Imagine, too, the real courage and determination of those who did enter the work force despite this handicap. Significantly, women nurses, not men, were the motivating force behind disposable sanitary protection.

Turn-of-the-century studies succeeded in convincing many women (and a few men) that their menstrual cycles need not be considered a disability. Clelia Duel Mosher's *Health and the Woman Movement* (1916) attempted to disprove the belief that increased activity would damage woman's health. Citing centuries of old wives' tales, she said:

Certainly, there is no disputing the fact that the mind has a powerful, if unconscious, control of organic processes. Now for generations, if we have taught girls any thing at all in regard to menstruation, we have been instilling the idea that it is a periodic illness involving suffering and incapacity.[6]

An especially convincing part of Mosher's thesis was her denunciation of women's clothing. Fashions, she found, were directly related to cramps. The heavy skirts and waist-pinching corsets of the nineteenth century would increase congestion and pain in the uterus, but "as the skirt grew shorter and narrower and the waist grew larger, the functional health of women improved." [7] She also devised a set of exercises to accompany the flapper fashions and free girls and women from menstrual pain.

Twenty years earlier, Mary Putnam-Jacobi, M.D., had also spoken out against the listlessness and enforced rest for women during menstruation, claiming that nothing but custom and the wishes of men were at the root of it:

> Thus one of the most essential apparent peculiarities of the menstrual process, its periodicity, that formerly was supposed to indicate the periodical increase in the vital forces of the female organism, has come to be considered as a mark of constantly recurring debility, decidedly as a fracture or paralysis.[8]

In their work, both women were actually trying to persuade women that no one need suffer menstrual pain against her wishes. This must have been a revolutionary idea for women, who had been convinced that ill health at menstruation was "woman's lot." The fact that women themselves perpetuated this belief is related to the eternal question of menstrual isolation: Who makes and enforces the taboos: men or women? In the industrial nineteenth century, just as in some prehistoric villages, menstrual malingering may have been subtly encouraged by men to ensure their dominance in the social and economic hierarchy. Woman, caught in this vicious circle of cause and effect, accepts her lot and makes the most of the benefits men see fit to extend to her, such as the protective labor laws, even if their real effect is to protect society from the achievements of women who work.

By the twentieth century, society showed more concern for the dollars and work hours lost because of menstrual and premenstrual absences than for the health and vitality of unborn children and their mothers. The protective laws themselves were used as evidence that women were incapable of holding responsible positions, from factory forewoman to company president. Grace Naismith, in *Private and Personal* (1966), uses unsupported statistics to prove that billions of dollars are lost each year because of women staying home from work with dysmenorrhea. She says:

> Since one out of every three workers in American industry today is a woman—24.5 million in our labor force—menstrual problems assume major significance. Eight percent of absenteeism is due to dysmenorrhea. The economic loss is said to be equivalent to an entire year of work by 58,000 women.[9]

To combat such waste, she suggests expanded use of industrial programs in which female employees are sent routinely to gynecologists ("sometimes a woman") to answer questions about their periods. She claims that Paramount Studios and United Artists require a gynecological exam for each employee, as do many other enlightened companies. If a woman (always an employee, never the boss) is absent too much, her (male) boss has a right to ask if she is menstruating or is "really sick," for "it is in the business world that menstruation plays havoc with men and their money."[10]

Naismith's book suggests that absenteeism caused by dysmenorrhea is all but out of control in twentieth-century America and that only the patient, kindly, fatherly bosses and gynecologists can save the economy from these bleeding subversives. Yet, every year, the U.S. Department of Labor statistics on absences from work prove this argument to be unfounded. In 1971, for example, men lost 5.1 days because of sickness or injury, and women lost 5.2. These figures remain about the same from year to year. That hardly heralds a massive breakdown of American industrial life, especially when coupled with the fact that women bear the responsibility for staying home with sick children—and husbands.

Another book with a similar argument is Katharina Dalton's *The Menstrual Cycle* (1969), which treats exhaustively the alleged effects on the economy of the emotional aspects of the premenstrual syndrome. Like Naismith, Dalton emphasizes an unproven correlation between menstruation and work loss but overlooks those studies and tests that tend to prove the opposite. [11] Especially important are the myriad of tests conducted in the private sector and the public as early as the 1920s, all showing little or no difference in efficiency and absenteeism among women during fluctuations of the menstrual cycle.

This same approach prevails in women's athletics. Historically, the menstrual cycle has been the root of discrimination against women in sports, despite the fact that in the last three Olympics, says an article in the September 1974 *Ms.*, "women won gold medals and established new world records during all phases of the menstrual cycle." Although there is a dearth of research involving women's psychological endurance or performance in sports, those studies that do exist find that menstruation has little or no effect. A recent study by the American Medical Association of sixty-six Olympic sportswomen showed that 75 percent continued regular training during menstruation, and only 5 percent stopped entirely. Unless a woman's period is unusually painful, says the AMA, "there seems to be no medical reason not to train or compete during menstruation." [12] Obviously, the menses did not interfere with the American Olympic swimmer who broke a world record and won three gold medals at the height of her period.

But, again, most of the popular reasons for discrimination are based on the *effect of the menstrual cycle on the sport.* For example, Dick Butera, owner of the Philadelphia franchise of the World Team Tennis League, was quoted in *Philadelphia* as saying that he plans to hire more women athletes than he needs at any one time: "What happens if Billie Jean wakes up the morning of a big match and she's got her period bad? What are you going to tell the fans?" [13]

One thing that an athlete *can* do if she "gets her period bad" is take hormones to delay it until after an important contest. Birth control pills can be used for this purpose, or the male hormone testosterone can be administered. Both Dalton and Naismith refer to the latter practice, but Dalton points out that the effects of testosterone on a woman's bodily strength and endurance are so extensive that the injection is illegal in most athletic contests. At Olympic Games, hormone tests are required of all athletes to make sure men aren't competing in women's contests.

Most women who are nonprofessional athletes probably formed their attitudes toward menstruation and sports in their high school gym classes, where they shared the experience of a character in Alice Munro's *Lives of Girls and Women:* "We had hidden in the girls' toilet together when we had the curse at the same time and were afraid to do tumbling—one at a time, in front of the rest of the class—afraid of some slipping or bleeding, and too embarrassed to ask to be excused." Such fears have bothered young women for centuries and originate in the two principles of menstrual politics we have been discussing: Girls in any condition do not participate in strenuous exercise because it might harm their female organs, and women cannot compete successfully in sports because their menstrual blood might "stain" the playing fields.

It is impossible to escape the conclusion that menstrual politics has dominated social and economic relations between the sexes since the beginning of time. In all their struggles for equality—the suffrage movement, the labor movement, the struggle for ERA—women have been obliged to fight against an enemy who will not contend with them in the halls of Congress or the courts of law. The enemy is within every woman, but it is not her menstruation. Rather, it is the habit of mind regarding menstruation into which she has been led by centuries of male domination. She has been taught that menstruation is disabling, and so she has been disabled.

Even in terms of twentieth-century life, it is inaccurate to say that women "invented" menstrual politics. Neither in machine-age America nor in contemporary Stone Age tribes have women had enough control over their own lives to manipulate and control the lives of the ruling men. As the servant learns to reinforce the prejudices of the master, so woman has learned well to echo the male menstrual prejudice born in fear of her mysterious functions.

Part Two

. . . .

THE MENSTRUAL CYCLE
IN ACTION

. . . .

Chapter 7

THE MENSTRUAL PROCESS

Menstruation is activated by the pituitary gland, which is located at the base of the brain. The pituitary releases a hormone called the *follicle-stimulating hormone* (FSH) at about midcycle. It also triggers the release of measured amounts of estrogen and progesterone in complementary curves throughout the month (so that when the level of one is the highest, the other is at its lowest). FSH also stimulates the ovaries, two glands about the size of almonds, as they prepare to release the eggs.

Each month, the left or the right ovary brings forth a ripening ovum, which bursts out of its sac, the graafian follicle. The egg's journey down the fallopian tube to the uterus is called *ovulation*. As the egg passes down the tube, it may meet with a sperm, unite, and form an embryo. This embryo will then imbed itself in the endometrium, the lining of the uterus, or womb. The imbedding is called *nidation* (literally, "nesting"). During the early stages of its development, the nested egg takes food from the endometrium, which has become thick and plushy, filled with watery fluids and blood. The neck of the womb will be sealed; no menstruation occurs during pregnancy, nor for as long as three to six months afterward. Breast-feeding may prevent the return of menstruation for an even longer time.

But if the egg travels down the tube unaccosted by a fertilizing sperm, then the enriched endometrium is not needed for food. The hormone estrogen, which supported the lining, soon stops its work. Progesterone takes over, stimulates the contraction of the uterus, and assists the velvety lining to leave through the vagina as menstrual "blood."

Menstrual fluid actually consists of more than blood; real blood makes up about one-half to three-quarters of the fluid, which also contains mucus, fragments of uterine mucous membrane, and scaling cell tissues from the vagina. Menstrual fluid has thirty times as much lime as regular blood and lacks ordinary blood's power to clot.

About midway between two periods, a physically mature woman will usually ovulate. The biological connection between menstruation and ovulation is a fairly new discovery and one that distinguishes the woman from other mammals. Less than a century ago, the menstruating woman was thought to be like an animal in heat (estrus). Animals at such times experience a discharge; they are also ovulating and are in their fertile period. But now we know that it is ovulation, not menstruation, that is closest to heat.

A woman may not be aware of any of the profound changes in her body over the course of her monthly cycle, but the possibilities for contrast are remarkable. Various studies have shown, for example, that a woman is less sensitive to pain while she ovulates, that her sense of smell improves, that her feelings of aggression and anxiety are low. Her hearing and sight are at their best, and she is more likely to feel elated. According to Kinsey's (disputed) study, 90 percent of women rate their own sexual arousal highest at midcycle. All these facts suggest that a woman will be most eager for sex at a time when she is most likely to conceive.

But about two weeks later, the menstruating woman might have cramps. She will be more prone to skin diseases, the most common being herpes (cold sores); acne, too, can be aggravated. Dark circles may appear under her eyes, and if she is susceptible to vaginal infections, this is the time when they may thrive because the vaginal atmosphere is less acidic.

Most of this monthly drama goes unnoticed by the average woman; a pimple on the nose will be lamented, of course, but the internal temperature and anxiety changes are more easily measured by scientific tests than by a woman's reactions. Sexual arousal is such a personal thing that many more women note their peak to be immediately before the menstrual period, possibly because of engorgement of genital tissues. The vast majority of women, in other words, regard the menstrual process in the proper light: as a normal, unremarkable biological process that may serve as a continuing reminder of their potential motherhood or may, on the other hand, be a nuisance welcome only at those times when motherhood, potential or actual, is merely an option in a woman's future program. Dark centuries of fear and taboo to the contrary, women, as opposed to men, are for the most part cheerfully and resignedly realistic about their periods.

Chapter 8

. . . .

THE FIRST POLLUTION: PSYCHOANALYSIS AND THE MENARCHE

Psychoanalytic studies of the trauma of the menarche and sub-sequent menstruations have been limited to patients, that is, women whose reactions are significantly aberrant from the normal woman's. In transposing these studies to generalized theories about women's attitudes toward menstruation, the assumption has been that menstruation itself is the aberrancy, that it is a bloody sign of women's loss of a penis, that it remains for all women in all times a sign of their uncleanliness and inferiority. In the major psychoanalytic writings, the menarche is generally seen as a curse associated with penis envy, castration anxiety, female masochism, and a potpourri of other psychic disorders. The psychoanalyst Otto Fenichel calls the menarche "the first pollution." [1]

Sigmund Freud makes a number of references to menstruation, although he develops no extensive theory about it. Early in his career, he used hypnosis to regulate a patient's menstrual cycle (2: 57).[2] In his essay "The Taboo of Virginity" (3: 198–99), he suggests that some women make a subconscious connection between the menstrual flow and defloration, thus implying physical violation or damage. In *Interpretation of Dreams*, he views red camellias as a symbol for menstruation. Freud's most imaginative statement about menstruation, however, is in *Civilization and its Discontents* (1930). Here, he examines the unpleasant effect of menstrual odor on the male psyche, a phenomenon that he attributes to man's shame when he began to walk on two legs; now that his genitals were out in the open, they became (logically?) something to be concealed, and any pleasure previously obtained from the sense of smell during intercourse now became taboo (21: 99). It would seem that at this historic moment, man's shame became woman's shame.

When Freud speaks specifically about the menarche, he usually compares it with the menopause. He views both events as internal (as opposed to external) crises in which the dammed-up libido, the source of psychic energy, can release disturbances ordinarily held in check (12: 236). Freud more or less expects someone who was not normally neurotic to become so at those moments. Thus, one psychoanalytic view of the menarche comes to parallel the instinctive fear of primitive peoples that menacing spirits, uncontrollable except by taboo, hover around a menarcheal or menopausal woman.

One of the earliest psychoanalytic works about menstruation is Mary Chadwick's *The Psychological Problems in Menstruation*, published in 1932. The section on the menarche describes the fears that Chadwick claims usually accompany the first menstruation. The adolescent girl is ashamed of her growing breasts and of her pubic hair, but her greatest shame is her menstrual blood: "She believes that she has injured herself, that it is some horrible disease, or that divine punishment has fallen upon her as retribution for former misdeeds." [3] After the first flow stops, the girl may fantasize that she is pregnant. She often revives the anal hate of childhood, the need to keep clean during the menses evoking painful recollections of diaper soiling and bed-wetting. She may indulge in self-torture or "morbid masturbation," although Chadwick does not specify exactly what morbid masturbatory techniques are most prevalent. The blood itself creates other fears: fears of castration, of separation, of bloodsucking, vampires, penis-breast identification, and witches.

A girl's ignorance of the menstrual process could surely

cause some of this distortion. Despite the barrage of educational materials now available to children, approximately 20 percent of adolescent girls are still uninformed about the menarche when it happens. We must also remember that Chadwick wrote this book more than forty years ago, when girls were generally more secretive and unknowledgeable about body functions than they are now. Yet, what to this day remains disturbing about Chadwick's book and others like it is the virtual absence of any positive statement concerning what to most pre-teens we know is an exciting, long-awaited, and much-discussed event.

One of the most influential theorists writing in the 1930s was Helen Deutsch. Like Freud, Deutsch regards both the menarche and the menopause as agitated periods during which previously repressed feelings are released.[4] The menarche is a disturbing event, she says, because for the first time in her life a girl is faced with "the double function of the female as a sexual creature and as a servant of the species" (1: 172), that is, as mother of the race. Deutsch views the adjusted adolescent as the one who accepts her subordinate status and, consequently, her female sexuality. But, Deutsch argues, if the menarche is met with resistance, the adolescent may have difficulty with what she calls her "final decision to be a woman" (1: 162).

The menstrual blood that brands the female as "servant of the species" is interpreted by Deutsch as an exclusively negative symbol. It represents, first of all, symbolic castration. The genitals bleed, reminding the adolescent that she has forever lost her wished-for and imagined penis. Deutsch contructed a theory based on her patients' fantasies without challenging its implications for her own sex, although she replaced Freud's "female castration complex" with the somewhat milder term *genital trauma.*

A second interpretation of women's psychological reaction to the menstrual flow, the one for which Deutsch is most noted, is the equating of lost blood with lost children. She assumes that all women want to be mothers. Thus, each menstruation is a dreadful disappointment because it indicates the failure to become pregnant. We find this idea restated by numerous analysts, among them Erik Erikson, who writes in his famous essay "Womanhood and the Inner Space" that a woman is most hurt when she is most empty: "Each menstruation . . . is a crying to heaven in the mourning over a child." [5]

Deutsch also notes that the first menstruation can signify a child's punishment for having played with her clitoris. Underlying this interpretation is the now-discredited Freudian assumption that clitoral stimulation is a regressive and self-indicting act which must eventually be abandoned for the mature, womanly vaginal orgasm.

Melanie Klein's discussion of the menarche in *The Psychoanalysis of Children* is based on equally negative assumptions. Klein says that the adolescent unconsciously identifies menstrual blood with urine and feces and thus with all their negative connotations. This is a fairly consistent idea in psychoanalytic theory, and it was probably first expressed by Ernest Jones, who discovered that girls who had never explored their vaginas often imagine that the menstrual flow and urine emanate from the same place.[6] Fear of bodily mutilation may also be experienced at the first sight of menstrual blood. Klein suggests that this phobia may arise because the girl has fantasized copulating with her father and fears her mother's revenge. Like Deutsch, Klein speculates that the blood is a sign that the potential child has been destroyed or, relying on Freudian theory, that the clitoris is an atrophied penis, that the clitoris is "the scar or wound left by her castrated penis." [7]

Castration anxiety is thus another common theme in psychoanalytic writing. Perhaps the most fear-ridden description of the castrating-castrated menstruating woman appears in Norman O. Brown's *Love's Body*, a book greatly influenced by the writings of Melanie Klein: "The vagina as a devouring mouth, or *vagina dentata;* the jaws of the giant cannibalistic mother, a menstruating woman with the penis bitten off, a bleeding trophy." [8]

Klein's single positive contribution to the psychology of menarche is that it may alleviate anxiety because it signifies the achievement of sexual status. The catch here is that the "feminine position" must have been carefully nurtured in the child as she grew to sexual maturity. It seems that in order to arrive at the "feminine position" a young girl must say to herself, "Yes, I'm mutilated. I'm a castrated male. I don't have the penis I always wanted. But I am very fortunate. I have the privilege of being a total woman. I shall bleed in the service of mankind."

This insistence on a total feminine identification is maintained by many recent theorists, among them Judith Bardwick, whose essays have been anthologized in *Woman in Sexist Society* and other feminist publications. Bardwick wrote in 1971 that although the "normal" adolescent will value the first menstruation as a sign of her femininity, the "neurotic who has rejected her sex will find the physiological changes of puberty traumatic because they challenge her repudiation of her sex." [9] Fleeing femininity, she may increase her efforts to gain a penis or castrate a male—at least symbolically.

When examining the causes of menarcheal disorders, most analysts tend to view the girl's mother as the chief source of the daughter's disturbance. Chadwick observed that children learned about menstruation from their mothers, many of whom spent two or three days a month in bed having headaches, being irritable, emitting foul odors. The realities of twentieth-century health and hygiene have probably obviated many of these traumas by now, but Chadwick suggests another idea that may still have some validity: because so many females are narcissistically concerned about staying young, they may resent their daughters' coming of age as a dismal reminder of their own approaching menopause.[10]

Deutsch, like Chadwick, states that the mother's uncleanliness and bad odor can create reactions of disgust in the daughter. Deutsch, however, also observes the mother's secrecy about her own menstruation, an attitude that seems far more prevalent than conscious carelessness. According to Deutsch, many mothers are more likely to talk to their daughters about conception, pregnancy, and birth than about menstruation (1: 152–157).

The analysts Karen Horney and Clara Thompson see society as the root cause of destructive attitudes in women. Horney also suggests that the mother's menstrual blood can reinforce the girl's discovery that women's bodies are extremely vulnerable; the girl may think that her mother has been injured in sexual intercourse.[11] (We wonder if the child who doesn't understand the meaning of menstrual blood is likely to know about sexual intercourse.) Thompson noted that learning about the menarche from an embarrassed or worried mother can cause negative reactions in the daughter, particularly when the mother uses the occasion to warn the girl about the dangers of becoming pregnant.[12] Probably the most extreme example of regarding the mother as the chief source for the daughter's menstrual difficulties occurs in an essay by Natalie Shainess, who argues that girls receiving no advanced knowledge have experienced "castration by the mother—the result of her omission of information." [13]

The mother is, of course, involved. Mothers who have learned to fear and resent their own bodies are likely to transfer negative feelings concerning menstruation to their daughters. However, it is crucial to emphasize, as few analysts do, that the society itself is primarily responsible for this internalized dread and that the mother, because she is presumed to be an exclusively sexual, childbearing, castrated, second-class animal, is herself a victim.

It is hard to find, in the psychoanalytic discussions of the menarche, a balanced conceptualization, one that presents the potentially positive as well as the inherently negative aspects of menstruation and one that accounts for the societal attitudes that underlie many of our feelings of disgust. We do find some ambivalence in the writings of Fenichel. While agreeing that menstrual disorders can signify "I have neither child nor penis," Fenichel nevertheless also stresses the purely biological aspects of menstruation that might cause discomfort or stress. In listing some of the unconscious meanings of menstruation, Fenichel includes the positive aspects of relaxation, genitality, and love, along with the more negative attitudes of "Oedipus guilt, castration, the frustration of wishes for a child, and humiliation." [14]

As early as 1926, Horney began to challenge some basic Freudian ideas about female sexuality, particularly the concepts of female castration and female masochism. Horney found among the patients she was treating a universal negativity toward the menstrual process; however, she is convinced that, although menstrual disorders can at times be an outlet for masochistic tendencies, this self-inflicted pain is not rooted in female anatomy alone but must be seen as "importantly conditioned by the culture-complex and social organization in which the particular masochistic woman has developed." [15] In other words, society has chosen to reward the bearer of the penis, not the loser of the blood, and then has interpreted the woman's unease with her inferior status as a "problem" that requires realignment of her personality in accord with the "norms" of society. Among the common traits of menarcheal girls, Horney lists lack of self-confidence, emotional detachment, the fear of being unattractive to men, the fear of being punished for masturbating, a loss of interest in work, and a development of homosexual tendencies. [16] The menarche, Horney admits, is a period of anxiety and stress primarily because the girl recognizes for the first time her vulnerability as a woman.

What distinguishes Horney's theory of the menarche from those of the other analysts is not, then, a positive attitude toward the menstrual process. Rather, it is her viewing menstrual difficulties within a broad social context. According to Horney (in the same paper), man devalues woman's functions in order to keep her out of his domain, creating an ideology that will keep him powerful and her inferior. The male sees the female as biologically incapable of assuming positions of power. This certainly is the theme that dominates intersexual relations among the primitives, and it clearly conditions the economics of the contemporary world.

Like Horney, Thompson calls into question the concepts of female castration and female masochism. Thompson insists that female sexuality must be discussed in nonmale terms, that women's bodies and minds must be seen in their own right. She points out, for example, that Freud based his observations of female masochism on a study of passive male homosexuals.

Among Thompson's own patients, there were a number of adolescents who were troubled during the menarche. One was an active, healthy child who, upon reaching puberty, was no longer allowed to go camping or hiking with her brother. "She was filled with bitterness and envy of her brother and for several reasons centered her whole resentment on the fact of menstruation. This seemed to be the sign of her disgrace, the sign that she had no right to be a person." This girl suffered, not from any fantasied hate or scarred and imagined wound, but from the fact that her first menstruation meant that her body and mind were to be restricted. She had not lost an imagined child or imagined penis. She had lost freedom, equality, and "the right to be aggressive." [17]

Thompson notes that positive advantages to reaching puberty, such as initiation into the important work of society and the passage into adulthood, have been devalued by our culture. Contemporary analysts suggest a few additional advantages. Judith Kestenberg, for example, speculated that the onset of menstruation "makes it possible for the girl to differentiate reality from fantasy." The regularity and "sharpness" of the menstrual experience leads to clear thinking and to a reorganization of the previously chaotic ego.[18] We find Kestenberg's account of renewed intellectual development at the menarche a phenomenon noted by many educators, more satisfying than the Freudian explanation offered by Chadwick and others: namely, that any marked intellectual achievement is a defensive reaction against the loss of the imagined penis.

Yet, the most influential psychoanalytic literature concerning menstruation continues to view this common and at times bothersome process as a "monthly neurosis" fraught with fears of castration, maternal revenge, anal repulsion, and lost children. The menarche, the first stage of this anxiety-ridden history, appears to be the first encounter in an intense psychic battle. The only "acceptable" action a woman can take is unconditional and immediate surrender to society's expectations.

Chapter 9

. . . .

THE STORM BEFORE THE CALM: THE PREMENSTRUAL SYNDROME

Perhaps in reaction to the negativism of traditional psychoanalytic thought about women, there is today a growing interest in the physical basis of menstrual disorders. Indeed, many researchers are convinced that all menstrual problems can be traced to a physical source, such as hormone-related water retention by the body's tissues. Others, however, insist that even if a psychological problem has a physical source, it remains necessary to treat the mental symptoms as well as the physical.

Two major groups of symptoms bother women immediately before and during menstruation. The physical sensations of cramping, bloatedness, backache, and the like are called *dysmenorrhea*, signifying an abnormality in the normal biological process; the mental symptoms of irritability or depression that tend to precede the period are grouped together in the term *premenstrual syndrome* (PMS). All these symptoms, physical and emotional, are part of the total biology and psychology of the menstruating woman and indeed may spring from the same physiological source.

In the second century A.D., when Soranus wrote his treatise for midwives, it was recognized that women were tense right before their periods. Not until 1931, however, did scientists invent a name for the tension. Karen Horney called it *Die Premenstruellen Verstimmungen* and said that women got it because they were denying the wish to be pregnant. The American gynecologist Robert Frank called it *premenstrual tension* and said that women got it because of an increase in the production of the female hormone estrogen.[1] It has also been called *premenstrual distress* (a minor disorder), the *premenstrual syndrome* (a generally more serious disorder), and the *premenstrual tension syndrome* (PTS). To avoid confusion, we shall call the difficulties experienced immediately before the period the *premenstrual syndrome* (PMS), and we include in that category both major and minor symptoms.

We believe that premenstrual symptoms are experienced to a lesser or greater extent by most women and that these symptoms are real rather than imaginary. We do not think, however, that PMS is, as some have argued, either a disease or a neurosis. It is so widespread a phenomenon, in fact, that the absence of the most common symptoms during the premenstruum would be unusual.

The premenstruum occurs shortly before the menstrual flow begins, usually within two or three days. The most common mood indicator for this phase is a feeling of tension, rather like a clock that has been wound too tightly. Besides feeling tense, women in their premenstrual phase are reported to feel irritable, faint, restless, sluggish, crabby, impatient, depressed, lethargic, deluded, indecisive, dizzy, nervous, nymphomaniacal, and irrational—although not all at once. The most common physical symptoms include swelling of the breasts, feet, abdomen, and vulva; hoarseness; constipation; hemorrhoids; skin eruptions such as cold sores or acne; weight gain (around three to six pounds); easy bruising; migraines; backaches; graying of hair; and peeling of fingernails. Dr. Katharina Dalton, who for the last decade has been accumulating statistics about the perils of premenstrual women, says that a tendency toward puffy skin and rings under the eyes has led some film stars to prohibit close-ups during menstruation or the premenstruum. Office assistants, on the other hand, slop coffee in saucers on these "off days," according to Dalton.[2]

A less common disorder associated with the premenstruum, but one of significance in the attempts to establish the syndrome as legal grounds for insanity, is spontaneous hypoglycemia. This condition, caused when blood-sugar values fall below the normal level, is similar to an overdose of insulin. Symptoms of hypoglycemia are nervousness, sweatiness, trembling, a craving for sweets; in extreme instances, which are rare, the spontaneous hypoglycemia of the premenstrual phase is marked by disassociation and other mental disturbances, coma, convulsion, and even death.

Frequently, the premenstrual woman will experience a tremendous surge of energy, coupled with an inability to direct this energy into productive channels. Some women take on huge tasks immediately before their period, tasks that are nearly impossible to complete. Housewives often display an intense urge to do major housecleaning. This increased spurt of energy is less characteristic of the phase, however, than the symptoms of sluggishness or lethargy.

During the premenstruum, women's dreams may reflect more anxiety and frustration than at other times. In 1968, Judith Bardwick and Melville Ivey studied twenty-six "normal" female college students during two consecutive cycles in order to determine the extent of premenstrual anxiety. They found that twenty-one of the twenty-six women scored higher in death anxiety, diffuse anxiety, mutilation anxiety, and shame anxiety during the premenstrual as opposed to the ovulatory phase of the cycle. They also noted among their subjects certain "premenstrual themes": inadequacy, hostility, incestuousness, death, fear of accidents; whereas the same subjects during ovulation expressed joy, peacefulness, achievement, fertility, and self-confidence. In one unusual instance, a subject expressed anxiety on the fourteenth day of her cycle. The next day she menstruated, two weeks early.[3]

For most women, the symptoms of the premenstrual phase are minor. They do not always occur, and when they do, they are almost unobservable. The most universal discomforts are bloatedness, irritability, and depression. In some instances, however, the woman may become violent, psychotic, or suicidal during the two to three days preceding her period. More commonly, she may be quarrelsome or irrational, characteristics that in the popular mind are erroneously associated with the menstrual rather than the premenstrual phase, as in the familiar observation, "She's acting crazy; she's got the rag on." Women who have severe premenstrual symptoms would be wise to consult a physician, although not necessarily Dr. Steincrohn, who writes in his health column (*Baltimore Sun*, June 14, 1973):

> This almost unbelievable change from a Sweet Sue to Horrible Hannah for one week before her periods is what breaks up many homes. If, instead of making a beeline for an attorney's office, the couple would first consult an understanding doctor, they might save themselves much grief.

How universal is so-called premenstrual tension? Estimates of sufferers range from 20 percent to 100 percent of women. But (and this is the same problem found with the psychoanalytic studies of menstruating women) many of the statistics on the severity of PMS do not adequately reflect the society at large because they are based on doctors' evaluations of their patients, frequently women in mental institutions. And of course, a major problem with premenstrual studies is that they fail to account for environmental pressures, which in many cases intensify the symptoms.

Several studies show that PMS is most intense in women between the ages of thirty and forty; others find it intensifies with successive pregnancies. Common sense would show that this is the age when women are "making it" (or not) in their careers and in their families. The children of a thirty-three-year-old mother are old enough to be making constant demands on her time; she may be involved in community affairs, the PTA, and cub scouts; and if she also is struggling to finish a degree or establish herself in her profession, the pressures on her are enormous. On the other hand, a Washington, D.C., gynecologist told us that he almost never sees severe cases of PMS in women who work outside the home; nor do the young daughters of these women experience any dysmenorrhea. The psychologist Karen Paige has found that women who are most distressed premenstrually are the ones most tied to home, children, and traditional maternal roles.[4]

ORIGINS OF PMS

Just as many psychiatrists have said that painful menstruation is in a woman's head, so have they said that premenstrual symptoms are "nervous" disorders and reflect a failure to adjust to woman's role, which they see as primarily reproductive. In the pioneer psychoanalytic essay on PMS, Karen Horney suggested that the tension preceding the period is caused by the unconscious denial of a desire for a child. Horney found the premenstrual phase to be a burden only for those patients who had conflicts about mothering.[5]

Treating PMS as a psychological problem goes back to the nineteenth century, but not until 1942 were the first extensive psychological tests conducted on menstrual and premenstrual women. Therese Benedek and B. B. Rubenstein examined the emotional and hormonal swings of the menstrual cycle and found a tendency toward acute emotional response and dependent behavior during the premenstruum, which they attributed to changes in the production of estrogen and to certain psychological factors.[6]

Since 1942, many attempts have been made to evaluate the premenstrual symptoms, but psychologist Mary Brown Parlee later concluded that there is *no* established proof that a measurable PMS even exists.[7] The correlational studies and the *Premenstrual Distress Questionnaire* results of Moos in 1968 often predict, through their wording, the very symptoms that they expect to isolate. Most of the studies on violence and PMS fail to place women in appropriate subgroups (for instance, criminals or artists). And in almost every case that involves proving PMS, a nonmenstruating (i.e., male) control group is absent. Parlee suggests, as do Lennane and Lennane,[8] that menstrual dysfunctions are more likely to have physiological than psychological origins.

Looking more widely for the causes of emotional changes during the premenstruum, the sociologist Karen Paige argues that premenstrual and menstrual blues are the result of cultural conditioning. Paige interprets menstrual distress as a "social response" to menstruation rather than a reaction to shifts in hormonal balance. Paige found that when her subjects' actual flow decreased, their anxiety also decreased. She also found that religious training had a significant effect on PMS, which was most severe among Catholic women in her group. The women most likely to suffer dysmenorrhea or PMS were found among those Catholics interviewed who believe that "a woman's place is in the home" and who are not interested in careers for themselves. Jews were the next most anxious group, with Protestants the freest from menstrual pain. Paige's observation is in opposition to the most frequently given psychological explanation for painful menstruation: that it is a sign of woman's failure to establish a "feminine identity." It seems to us that a woman who spends all day in the house concentrating on her "womanly" duties will be much more inclined to notice and think about her changes in weight and emotion than one whose mind is occupied with extra-female things. Another point made by Paige is that none of the symptoms associated with premenstrual or menstrual depression is unique to menstruation or, for that matter, to women.

Yet, the fact remains that many women do get headaches or the blues right before their periods, even those who are convinced that woman's place is not exclusively in the home. The sociological theory of PMS too readily dismisses undisputed evidence of hormonal changes triggering water buildup in the tissues, a physical condition that can produce most of the emotional conditions we have enumerated.

The most plausible theories about the origins of PMS center on the production of and tenuous balance between the hormones estrogen and progesterone in the female body. We have already noted that the pituitary regulates these hormones and that as the level of estrogen peaks and then falls just before the onset of the period, the level of progesterone, triggered by ovulation, rises. It is progesterone that is the water-retaining hormone. And fluid retention seems to be at the root of most of the evils of the premenstruum.

When there is too much water in the tissues, it shows up as general bloatedness, swelling of the hands, feet, and legs; it can also cause dark, puffy rings around the eyes. Even the brain tissues retain water, and the accumulated body tension from all these causes produces a pressure that is easily translated into emotional stress, especially, we think, when combined with the nuisance of menstrual bleeding and the sexual abstinence that usually accompanies the period. Although there has been some confusion in the medical literature over which hormone (estrogen or progesterone) has the more direct effect on a woman's emotions, a gynecologist told us that balanced concentrations of the two hormones help preserve, rather than disturb, a woman's emotional equilibrium during the premenstruum.[9]

CURES FOR PMS

A consensus of medical experts shows that the easiest and most sensible solution to the problems of the premenstruum is to eat well, particularly to reduce the intake of salt and fluid during the premenstruum. One's food should be high in protein, low in carbohydrates; a high-protein diet will do as much as any other regimen to maintain a normal fluid balance in the body by facilitating the oxidation and excretion of food. A high-protein diet will also help keep the blood-sugar level stable. The reduction in blood sugar that accompanies the premenstruum can produce an irresistible urge for sweets, which provide only temporary relief of fatigue and listlessness. And the same blood-sugar drop can make women more susceptible to the effects of alcohol.

Regular exercise will help carry off body fluids in the form of perspiration. Exercise also keeps the abdominal muscles in good working order and prevents the congestion that so often leads to cramps during the first or second day of the period. And both good diet and regular exercise will help prevent constipation, another source of misery to the already full and bloated abdomen.

Birth control pills can reduce PMS. One gynecologist told us that approximately 25 percent of his patients who take the pill do so primarily to ease PMS or dysmenorrhea. The usefulness of the pills is based on the fact that they establish a false pregnancy in the reproductive organs, so that although a woman continues to menstruate, she is not really experiencing a menstrual cycle.

Basically, the pills employ a combination of estrogen and progesterone in proportions that approximate the hormonal conditions of pregnancy. As in pregnancy, the pituitary gland is not stimulated to release FSH; therefore, no egg is released; therefore, the ovulation part of the menstrual cycle never occurs. Because there is no ovulation, there is no corresponding rise in progesterone; with no rise in progesterone, the body's fluid level remains more or less constant. Furthermore, the lower progesterone level also prevents the contraction of the uterus that normally produces menstruation and possibly cramps. When a woman stops taking the pills after twenty days, the accumulated blood and tissue leave her uterus because there is nothing there to hold them, but the flow is not a true menstruation if we consider menstruation to be one part of a complex monthly cycle.

Although many different types of pills are on the market, each with a different combination of the two hormones, they all work in this basic way. Obviously, the absence of fluid buildup and uterine contraction alleviate the most common symptoms of the premenstruum and the early days of the period. Although there is well-documented evidence that these pills have dangerous side effects, and some women find that they diminish sexual pleasure, for those who are willing and able to take the risks, the pills are definitely beneficial in treatment of the normal but annoying symptoms of menstruation.

On the other hand, caffeine and epsom salts are two nonprescription drugs that help to reduce water retention. There are a number of premenstrual remedies on the market, including Trendar, Pamprin, Midol, Aqua-Ban, and Aquatabs. These pills are diuretics, and their major ingredients are caffeine and ammonium chloride. Some of them contain aspirin. Diuretics, although they relieve the physical symptoms of PMS, do not affect the mental symptoms. The pill does both.

MENSTRUAL SUPPRESSION

Removing the menses altogether through drugs has been suggested as a treatment for PMS, particularly for the severely retarded or for mental patients. If we remember Karen Paige's findings that the more diminished the flow, the less intense the premenstrual symptoms, menstrual suppression would seem a valid alternative to the menses in some cases. Of course, continued use of birth control pills can help a woman achieve this same effect; this practice, although relatively harmless on occasion (one's wedding day, a big sports competition), would undoubtedly increase the risks of dangerous side effects if prolonged. As far as we know, there have been no extensive studies or tests of such continuous usage.

More than a few gynecologists practice still another form of menstrual suppression: hysterectomy. A woman whose PMS is severe can easily find a doctor who will remove her uterus, thus eliminating the organ that is the focus of menstrual and premenstrual problems. Even though a hysterectomy may not be indicated for a serious medical reason, such as cancer, a precancerous condition, or deterioration of the endometrium, the operation has been performed to eliminate PMS.

Some clinicians see PMS as a response to anticipated sexual denial. Because women usually refrain from intercourse during their periods, they feel nervous or frustrated immediately before, and of course during, their days of abstinence. Paige's research would support this hypothesis. Paige found that women who had few negative attitudes toward sexual intercourse during their periods (about 50 percent of the Protestants in her sample) were the ones with the lowest incidence of PMS.

PREMENSTRUAL PITFALLS

Whatever the causes of PMS, and in spite of the increasing possibility of alleviating it for most women, the argument that the menstruating woman poses a threat to her society is still heard. The following statistics and studies proving the incompetence of *some* premenstrual women are cited repeatedly as evidence that *all* women function in inferior fashion when subject to Eve's curse.

The "Women at Work" chapter of Dalton's *The Menstrual Cycle* is a compendium of aches and pains experienced by premenstrual women who work outside the home. Secretaries fill wastebaskets with spoiled work, executives fire the wrong people, forewomen slow down the assembly line, and factory workers stay home. This chapter gives apparent scientific support for Dr. Edgar Berman's widely publicized remark: "If you had an investment in a bank, you wouldn't want the president of your bank making a loan under these raging hormonal influences at that particular period." [10]

Accidents and Suicide

In 1959, a study was done in England of 102 uteri collected from one of Her Majesty's morgues in order to determine at what phase of her cycle a woman is most prone to fatal accidents and to suicide. By examining the cells of the endometrium, the investigators found the peak danger phase to be not the premenstrual phase, as we might suspect, but rather what is called the *midluteal* phase (days 17 to 23). In the bleeding phase itself, there was only *1* suicide and *no* accidental deaths.[11] Dalton found, however, in a study of hospital admissions, that 53 percent of women admitted for emergency accident treatment were in the menstrual or premenstrual phase.[12] But one author has suggested, with refreshing logic, that the accident-proneness of the premenstrual phase might be caused by the drugs women take to reduce the symptoms.[13] Statistics, as usual, can be marshaled to support either side.

One early study of accidents and the menstrual cycle teaches us a lesson in how scientific "evidence" can lead to discrimination against women. The investigator, who worked for the Department of Commerce, was disturbed by an increasing number of accidents among women pilots: "The United States have been practically depleted of women pilots by accidents," the investigator claimed. Of the three specific accidents he looked into, the three pilots were in fact menstruating (rather than *pre*menstruating). In one, the plane was so demolished that "no satisfactory examination could be made of the control system." Of course, the control system would not have been menstruating.

The investigator did not insist that women be banned from the skies during their periods, but they should, he suggested, be aware of their weaknesses and ground themselves if they have problems. "If they are not able to evaluate their frailties while on the ground," he asks, "how are they going to evaluate them in the air?" [14]

The essay includes no assessment of the premenstrual phase, perhaps because it would have been harder for the investigator to establish proof. Nor does he compare the ratio of female accidents with that of male accidents. Nor does he consider such contributing factors as weather or control system malfunctions. Yet, in 1934, when this essay was written, women were being removed from the skies as pilots and going back up as stewardesses.

Suicides

Of the 102 women whose uteri were subjected to Her Majesty's microscopes, most of those who committed suicide did so during the midluteal phase, with carbon monoxide poisoning being the leading cause of death. In a 1968 study of fifty-nine (live) women who had deliberately injured themselves, the researcher found a "premenstrual excess," defining premenstrual to include the seven days before the menses.[15] The most enlightening fact of this study is that premenstrual suicide attempts were most frequent among women who lived with a man. Fifty-six women who called the Saint Louis Suicide Prevention Center in 1971 also were predominantly premenstrual.[16]

The most statistically convincing connection between suicide and menstruation comes from Nairobi, Kenya, where, between 1958 and 1960, a doctor performed necropsies on twenty-two Hindu women who burned themselves to death and found that nineteen were menstruating at time of death and two were pregnant. Of three African women who hanged themselves, the same doctor discovered that all three were menstruating.[17]

In evaluating any demonstrated relationship between suicide and menstruation, we must keep in mind the fact that suicide rates among women are considerably lower than suicide rates among men. The 1973 *Information Please Almanac*, for example, lists not one country in which female suicides exceed male suicides. The highest percentage of female suicides among the places listed is in West Berlin, and even there, only slightly over 30 percent of total suicides are females. To our knowledge, no studies have been made of periodicity in male suicides.

In none of the studies of suicide and the menstrual cycle does the investigator examine the environmental situation surrounding the suicide. Had the premenstrual or menstrual woman been beaten by her husband or lover before attempting suicide? Had she been fired from her job? Had she been drinking? Had the Hindu women set themselves aflame for political reasons? Had it been raining for several weeks? We learn from A. Alvarez's book on suicide, *The Savage God*, that the poet Sylvia Plath committed suicide during one of the coldest winters London had ever known. She was suffering from sinus problems, loneliness, depression, and cold. All the pipes in her flat had frozen solid. She had just come back from a weekend. She had no telephone. She was unable to reach her psychiatrist. There were at least fifty-nine other suicides in London that week, the weather being a major factor.[18]

Emile Durkheim, in his classic study *Suicide* (1897), *does* consider the effects of women's rhythms (along with the effects of aging, childlessness, widowhood, and divorce) on female suicides. He finds that the "sexual cycle" does *not* affect the suicide rate among women and offers a sociological explanation: "Woman kills herself less, and she kills others less, not because of physiological differences from man, but because she does not participate in collective life *in the same way*." [19]

Crime, Insanity, and the Law

In her study "Menstruation and Crime," Dalton interviewed newly convicted women and women in prison who had been reported for bad behavior while jailed. She found that 49 percent of the crimes were committed menstrually or premenstrually, with theft being the most frequent (56 percent), alcoholism second (54 percent), and prostitution third (44 percent). Dalton explains that criminals were convicted most frequently in the premenstruum because slow reaction time and "mental dullness" made getting caught more likely.

Most other studies of the type support some correlation between menstruation and crime. But it is crucial to emphasize, as in the suicide studies, that women's crimes are far fewer than men's crimes. From a 1973 FBI report published in the 1975 *Information Please Almanac,* we learn that men commit 94.6 percent of all burglaries and 92.0 percent of all crimes involving possession of dangerous weapons. Women, on the other hand, commit 75.5 percent of crimes involving prostitution and commercialized vice, 31.5 percent of all larceny and theft, 26.7 percent of forging and counterfeit crimes, 34.2 percent of vagrancy crimes, 31.2 percent of all frauds, and 55.5 percent runaways. In all other areas, from a total of thirty categories, women commit well under 25 percent of the crimes in this country. In light of these statistics, the menstrual cycle becomes a minimal consideration.

Menstrual irregularities have frequently been associated with insanity, particularly with postpartum depression and schizophrenia. In a study conducted in the early 1930s, it was discovered that acutely disturbed women are often "exhibitionistic" about their menstrual blood. One "cyclothymic" woman had a habit of throwing "blood-stained sanitary napkins out of windows to boys"; another woman liked to smear herself with menstrual blood, which she called "the blood of Jesus Christ." [20] Many contemporary psychiatrists would argue that a schizophrenic's actions have meaning in terms of the society which oppresses her. These napkins, then, become a mark of defiance against a world that devalues and oppresses women.

Among women who have experienced extreme postpartum depression, there is sometimes a tendency for the psychotic episode to recur premenstrually once the menses has resumed. Repetition of psychotic behavior during the premenstrual phase was also observed in a twenty-one-year-old black college student who was declared "sick" when she became abusive to her teachers and "began to use words in German which she had incidentally learned." The student was given shock treatment by her white male doctors for her premenstrual disorder. Another black woman, a patient of the same doctors, was given a series of eight shock treatments to cure her premenstrual disorientation. The symptoms nevertheless returned during her next premenstruum but eventually disappeared after she was treated with drugs.[21]

Because of long-established connections between psychosis and PMS, some forensic psychiatrists have argued that severe and ascertainable premenstrual disorders should be considered grounds for the insanity plea. The French have long viewed PMS as grounds for temporary insanity, although Americans have not.

In 1953, a New York law professor made a strong case for the premenstrual syndrome as a legal defense. Arguing that the hypoglycemic factor of the premenstruum can account for "impairment of self control" and for "moral insanity," the professor insisted that the law must deal with PMS, just as it must deal with "the phenomenon of insanity or gravity." [22] In a counterargument, another lawyer claimed that it is "totally misleading" to connect "a procedure such as a vaginal smear with a person's legal responsibility." [23] A vaginal smear, it seems, is one of the proofs of PMS that the defendant would be expected to produce in court.

In a lengthy essay written in 1971,[24] Aleta Wallach and Larry Rubin analyze medical data and legal precedent in order to establish PMS as a plea for "diminished capacity," meaning that the defendant did not at the time of the crime have a specific criminal intent. They also suggest that PMS would be useful in plea bargaining (pleading guilty to a lesser charge in order to get a reduced sentence). Wallach and Rubin base their argument on a number of complex issues and past rulings. One of their strongest points is that the chromosomal imbalance known as the XYY syndrome, a genetic defect in men, has been successfully used as a defense; yet PMS, which they define as an organic disorder, has been largely ignored in legal writings. They emphasize that the defense would have the most chance of success in the state of California, where the attitude toward temporary insanity is more flexible than in other states and where the plea of "diminished capacity" has legal precedent.

Wallach and Rubin anticipate one of the basic objections to their argument: namely, that PMS would then become a *legal* justification for discrimination against women. They stress that PMS is an organic disease only for some women, not for women as a class, and that those women who do have severe mental disturbances during the premenstrual phase deserve the protection of the law. Nor do they think that a woman would have to provide a case history of premenstrual disorders before the court. Because the medical profession has for years been treating the syndrome as imaginary, they argue that it would be unreasonable to expect a woman to provide evidence of treatment in establishing the syndrome as an alibi.[25]

We think it likely that a judge would demand proof if PMS were used as a defense. The defendant would probably be asked to furnish evidence of a past history of premenstrual disorders, and she would have to prove that she was in the premenstrual phase of her cycle when the crime was committed. This record would entail visits to a psychiatrist and submission to laboratory tests. But perhaps the greatest discomfort would occur in the courtroom, where the woman's menstrual cycle would become public information. Given the public silence on this subject, a defendant might be reluctant to employ PMS in her defense. If she bravely spoke about her menstrual cycle in court, the jury, which would be likely to believe many of the cultural myths about menstruation, might be unsympathetic.

Real as the premenstrual symptoms are, it seems to us that enshrining them in the legal system of the United States would pose more problems than it would solve. At a moment in history when the Equal Rights Amendment is looked upon as the great eraser of all statutory distinctions between the sexes and the only hope for women's equality before the law, such a step would be regressive.

WEATHERING THE STORM

There is one final alternative to the problem of PMS, one that is diametrically opposed to menstrual suppression. Rather than reduce or eliminate the menses, that visible sign of woman's otherness, we could instead psychologically embrace the blood that is ours, making of menstruation an affirmation instead of a denial. There is at work in our bodies a menstrual dialectic, a complicated shift of rhythms, a tension and then a release from tension. The more conscious we become, the more fully we can sense these rhythms, the more self-knowledge we shall achieve. As Nancy Milford has written: "There is something of unalterable value in woman's experience: the very cyclical motion of her body makes her life marked by upheaval, change and discharge. I am not willing to say that she is more vulnerable because of it, but that it is instead a source of potential strength; change need not stun her or threaten her, for she is in constant flux." [26] To reject and eliminate the body processes, to let our moods be dampened through progesterone or estrogen or testosterone, is in part to agree with those who hold that womanhood is an inferior state of being.

One of the acknowledged symptoms of PMS is a sharp increase in drive and energy. Some women enjoy this drive and energy; they find it creative. Premenstrual tension can mean, depending on who is defining it, an acuteness of sensibility and a sharpening, rather than a dulling, of intelligence. It can be a time for directing our hormonally induced irritability into significant social action that will challenge the society that would curtail our movement and keep us grounded.

Tests, graphs, and questionnaires by the dozens have been designed to show the extent of woman's premenstrual or menstrual misery. Yet Parlee is one of the few researchers to question the soundness of such questionnaires, which she claims reflect a bias toward treating menstruation as a problem and which in effect measure stereotypical beliefs. Parlee is working on new kinds of psychological tests, ones that would measure a woman's premenstrual strengths rather than her premenstrual tensions.[27]

We believe that with a more positive attitude toward female processes, researchers could begin to view PMS in an altogether different framework. In the case of the *Menstrual Distress Questionnaire* devised by Rudolf H. Moos in 1969, for example, the title reveals quite clearly that the attitudes will be negative. Of the forty-seven items in the questionnaire, only *five* predict positive results, for example, "feelings of well-being" or "bursts of energy or activity." The other forty-two questions measure menstrual distress, for example, "avoid social activities" or "decreased efficiency." [28] The

MENSTRUAL JOY QUESTIONNAIRE

Name _____ Occupation _____

Age _____ Today's date _____

Below is a list of pleasures which women sometimes experience. Kindly evaluate your experience of these pleasures during the three different stages listed below:

    A. During your most recent menstrual flow
    B. During the week preceding your menstrual flow
    C. During the remainder of your cycle

Write the number in each space which corresponds most accurately to your experience:

    1 = none
    2 = hardly noticeable
    3 = mild
    4 = moderate
    5 = strong
    6 = acute

NOTE: In answering the questionnaire, reflect the experiences of your *most recent* cycle.

	A. most recent flow	B. week before	C. remainder of cycle
1. High spirits	_____	_____	_____
2. Increased sexual desire	_____	_____	_____
3. Vibrant activity	_____	_____	_____
4. Revolutionary zeal	_____	_____	_____
5. Intense concentration	_____	_____	_____
6. Feelings of affection	_____	_____	_____
7. Self-confidence	_____	_____	_____
8. Sense of euphoria	_____	_____	_____
9. Creativity	_____	_____	_____
10. Feelings of power	_____	_____	_____

questionnaire, because of its overwhelmingly negative emphasis, is bound to show negative results.

If the questionnaire were called the *Menstrual Joy Questionnaire,* if the majority of items asked for responses such as "happiness" or "feeling great" or "able to plot effective strategy" or "increased creativity," the end results would inevitably be different. We have learned from the many studies on suicide, that woman's suicide attempts occur at a "certain" time of the month, although at what time is rarely consistent. There are no studies, to our knowledge, of creativity or good works during the premenstruum. Who knows what suffragist and feminist strategy was initiated during Elizabeth Cady Stanton's or Lucy Komisar's premenstrual phase? What day did Billie Jean King have circled on her calendar when she massacred Bobby Riggs with her drive, energy, aggressiveness, and self-control? (It is said that King had hypoglycemia a week before the match.)

These questions, which cannot be asked in a vacuum or answered in a laboratory, are the kinds of issues that historians and psychologists must bring into the open if they are to assess the effects of PMS on women's public and private lives. Tests, graphs, and questionnaires by the dozens have been designed to determine the extent of woman's incompetence. Now we need to measure a woman's premenstrual strength.

Part Three

THE MENSTRUATING WOMAN IN THE POPULAR IMAGINATION

Chapter 10

"WHAT EVERY GIRL SHOULD KNOW"

There is a community of experience among women who have come of age in twentieth-century America. Conversations about The First Time seem to be punctuated with "You, too?" or "Wait'll you hear how *I* found out . . . !" We release our precious "dirty" secrets and laugh in relief when we are understood, for those adolescent attempts to understand what the "glory of womanhood" was all about were thwarted on every side by euphemisms. From the anxious comparisons among the eleven-year-olds to the tight-lipped acknowledgments of some mothers that, "Yes, Virginia, you are a woman now," the play unfolding within our bodies has been spoken largely in whispers.

The coming of our periods might have been relatively normal events in the mixed-up teen years. But we learned quickly that however frankly menstruation might be discussed at home, the world did not want to hear of it. We live in a greeting-card culture where, for twenty-five cents, we can purchase socially approved statements about childbirth, marriage, or death. But Hallmark manufactures no cards that say, "Best Wishes on Becoming a Woman." Rather than celebrate the coming-of-age in America, we hide the fact of the menarche, just as we are advised to deodorize, sanitize, and remove the evidence. Even the booklets from Modess and Kotex (themselves monuments of greeting-card blandness), which we giggled over and learned by heart in the forbidden hours at slumber parties, were sent in plain brown wrappers.

We who grew up in the fifties think that these booklets were as important in shaping our permanent consciousness about menstruation, as the attitudes of our mothers and our friends. The message from the manufacturers, of course, was aimed at getting us to use more and more napkins, to send for "training kits" so we'd be prepared, paraphernaliawise at least, for the big day (becoming a woman in the United States involves education for consumerhood as much as the kiddie shows and their paper cereals do). But the message behind the ads was hard-sell shame: *Cover it up.* Use our product because "nothing will show"; "no one will know"; "your secret will be safe."

The information about menstruation available to our daughters, compared with what our mothers might have read, shows few changes: deodorize, sanitize, hide your shame, although some companies seem to be groping their way toward a more positive educational message.

In 1934, a female "Voice of Experience" gave the following advice to young readers: Girls should not exercise, play tennis, or wear high-heeled shoes during their periods; such activity can cause a prolapsed uterus. Girls should wear tight-fitting bloomers during the winter menstrual cycles; otherwise, they are likely to develop a "catarrhal condition" in the delicate vaginal tissues. The Voice of Experience discouraged cold or hot baths, swimming, horseback riding, "athletic dancing, lifting of heavy weights, doing arduous household duties, etc." The punishment for this sort of activity during the menstrual period includes fallen organs, irregular menstruation, and a "critical menopause." [1]

Most current advice books, far from forbidding exercise and baths, recommend lots of fresh air, exercise, and personal hygiene. In a pamphlet distributed by Kimberly-Clark, the makers of Kotex, a girl is assured that she can do everything during her period that she does during the rest of the month: shampoo her hair, go to gym class, shower, and dance. The pamphlet does not mention "arduous household duties." The booklets also tend to de-emphasize the actual bother of menstruation, although most perceptive adolescents can readily conclude, from all the instructions about keeping clean and changing napkins, that it can indeed be a messy business.

Another common theme in advice books is that menstruation means motherhood. In *A Doctor Talks to Teenagers*, the doctor urges his readers to view the menarche as a time for strengthening the maternal instinct. Men and women are equally intelligent, the doctor conceded, but "man's world is in the economic and industrial field, while woman's domain is in the higher spiritual activities of society and the home." [2]

But recognizing the childbearing aspect of menstruation when you are thirteen does not bring personal fulfillment, any more than a boy's first wet dream signals the glorious achievement of potential fatherhood. In *You and Your Daughter*, a pamphlet published by Kimberly-Clark in 1968, ovulation is discussed realistically, with the bearing of a child treated as a future possibility rather than an immediate joy. "The mere fact of menstruation does not always mean that a girl is mature enough to have babies—either biologically or psychologically" is the advice. "A young girl cannot become a mature full-fledged woman overnight."

The napkin manufacturers also obtain wide circulation for their educational films, which are generally based on their major pamphlets and are designed to be shown in schools. Kimberly-Clark has for about twenty years been floating a Walt Disney production called *The Story of Menstruation*. In the Disney world, the menstrual flow is not blood red but snow white. The vaginal drawings look more like a cross section of a kitchen sink than the inside and outside of a woman's body. There are no hymen, no clitoris, no labia; all focus is on the little nest and its potentially lush lining. Although Disney and Kimberly-Clark advise exercise during the period, the exercising cartoon girls (who look like Disney's Cinderella) are drawn without feet; bicycles magically propel themselves down the street without any muscular or mental direction from the cyclist. The film ends happily ever after, with a shot of a lipsticked bride followed immediately by a shot of a lipsticked mother and baby.

In *Naturally . . . a Girl,* a film produced by the Personal Products Company (Modess) for "girls 9–14 and their mothers," the drawings are more realistically done; however, there are still no cervix, clitoris, or labia. Boys as well as girls are included in the filmed discussions. The film ends with a series of shots of working women: lineswomen, cops, mothers, secretaries. The last words are: "It's better than being a boy!"

The minute sex becomes the school subject, boys and girls are separated. In the juvenile novel *Are You There God? It's Me, Margaret* (written by Judy Blume, who has also written the Personal Products Company's updated *Growing Up and Liking It*) an appropriately satiric treatment is given to these separate sex-ed classes. The sixth-grade girls attend a film, *What Every Girl Should Know,* sponsored by the PTA. "The film told us about the ovaries and explained why girls menstrooate, but it didn't tell us how it feels, except to say that it is not painful, which we knew anyway. Also it didn't really show a girl getting it. It just said how wonderful nature was and how we would soon become women and all that." [3]

During the PTA lecture, Nancy, one of Margaret's friends, asked the shocking question, "How about Tampax?" The advice giver's flustered response is, "We don't advise *internal protection* until you are considerably older." Prohibiting tampons to youngsters probably has little to do with discomfort or lack of accommodation but, rather, most likely reflects the fear that a girl may ruin her hymen, that magical tissue of flesh that never gets shown in the how-to-insert folders. In the book *Our Bodies, Ourselves,* an illustration actually shows six different hymens, or maidenheads. The Boston Women's Health Collective, which wrote the book, takes aim at the myth that tampons can be used only after losing one's virginity. They explain that there are openings in the hymen through which the fluid flows and through which it is, except in rare cases, quite possible to insert a tampon. [4]

Few advice books or pamphlets are so honest. Few films or illustrations show, as *Our Bodies, Ourselves* does, a hymen or a clitoris, both of them parts of a woman's anatomy. And few books are so direct in talking about the realities of the menstrual process.

Are You There God . . . and *Our Bodies, Ourselves* indicate a possible change of direction. Another is the attempt, albeit thwarted, to initiate a To Be a Woman badge for girl scouts. This badge was proposed by the Philadelphia Girl Scout Council and would have included the scouts' learning about a number of topics of vital importance to them: menstruation, abortion, contraception, rape, and job discrimination. As one of their assignments, they would have been required to discuss menstruation with their mothers and grandmothers. One of the mothers who helped defeat the proposal commented: "Being a Girl Scout means baking cookies for old ladies on Christmas and watering the plants at the railroad station." [5]

This controversial matter will emerge again, not only in Philadelphia but in rural areas, not only among the Girl Scouts of America but among the 4-H clubs, the Y-Teens, the Camp Fire Girls. For, like Margaret, young women know that they can swim and dance and use tampons if they want to without any serious physical or psychological damage. But even this minimal amount of knowledge and openness about menstruation has had to break through strong barriers of innuendo and taboo.

Chapter 11

. . . .

THE MONTHLY EUPHEMISM

One of the notable qualities of menstruation is its democracy. No respecter of class lines, no quibbler with standards of decency, it strikes all women in all walks of life.

The menstrual consciousness expressed in literature and psychoanalysis is likely to be that of an individual sensibility, that is, the response of one artist or doctor to a woman's monthly bleedings. But the materials of popular culture, the jokes and advertisements, because they are anonymous or at least unattributed, are much better clues to mass psychology, to what "the people" think.

Several common themes appear in popular verbal expressions used with menstruation.[1] Time and regularity, blood and redness are the most obvious factors, but expressions are also likely to refer to visitors, to illness or inconvenience, and to male or female persons. And especially in American slang— more open, less inhibited than that of most other cultures— there are references to menstrual paraphernalia and to the taboo against sex during menstruation.

The number of menstrual expressions in a language often indicates the society's attitudes toward women's periods. The more openly the subject is accepted, the more words there are. In a study made in 1947 and 1948, Natalie F. Joffe found that Irish, English, Polish, and Yiddish had very scanty menstrual vocabularies, but that there was an abundance of expressions in German, Italian, and French and a flood of Americanisms.

If common expressions indicate what is most obvious and noticeable, then one of the most obvious facts about menstruation is that it keeps coming back every month, as in the Italian "the month," the Yiddish "the monthly time," the Polish "every month," the Irish "in season," the German "the time," the English and American "it's her time of the month" and "the monthlies." In French, menstruation is *les règles* ("the rules"), for its regularity.

The monthly visitation is frequently referred to as a visitor, particularly a red one, such as a "red aunt." In German (as in Yiddish) the visitor is "the red king" or the "tailor" or is called by a name, Frederick Barbarossa. Visitor expressions may date back to the Middle Ages; Frederick Barbarossa (red beard) lived in the twelfth century. Although their country no longer has an official ruling family, Italian women may still visit "the magnificent marquis." The French may say, "I have Jacques" (or "François" or "Martin"), or "I am going to see Sophie," or "I am having the painters," or "I am going to see my relatives at Montrouge" (literally, "red mountain").

The French sometimes use phrases that express their xenophobia. A Frenchwoman may "have the English" ("redcoats") or "Garibaldians" ("redshirts"), or she may see the "landing of the English," an ironic expression also stemming from the Middle Ages, when an English debarkation usually meant a bloody massacre.

Redness and blood are recognized in ways that are devious and ways that are explicitly crude. The French speak of periods as "cardinals" and "tomatoes" and of the menstruating female as *la femme fraise des bois* (literally, "the strawberry woman"). Italian women may travel "the red road" or may say they are "losing blood." Polish women have "leakage" or "flow."

American women may visit "my redheaded aunt from Red Bank," may have "a red-letter day," may say "I'm Bloody Mary today," or "the Red Sea's out." Yet, American males are more likely than females to refer to red or blood; in the 1940s, they used jive talk: "The chick is a Communist"; "dirty red"; "her cherry is in sherry." And although the French might say *les fleurs* ("flowers") and American Indians "time of flower," preserving the very old association between periods and flowers, American navy men after World War II reduced flowers to the lowest common denominator; in their vernacular, the menstruating woman was characterized as "a snatch box decorated with red roses."

Nineteenth-century expressions tend to hide the physical facts of menstruation behind euphemisms: "sickness," "unwell," "poorlies," "indisposed." But modern American popular language is apt to be much more graphic. Although "the curse" and "falling off the roof" are not very explicit, other expressions openly celebrate menstrual paraphernalia or bemoan the intercourse taboo. A tampon may be simply a "plug," but sanitary napkins are more grandly described: "cotton horsies," "Mickey Mouse mattresses." The menstruating woman may be "riding the rag" or "have the rag on"; she may bear a "manhole cover"; she may also "ride the cotton pony" or "the cotton bicycle." Because "ketchup" is used as a term for the blood, and "sorority juice" was once a college students' term for ketchup, an astute observer in the 1940s might have remarked, "Too much sorority juice down there." Other indications of sexual unavailability are "the flag is up" (referring to the red flag on rural mailboxes), "ice-boxed," "Mickey Mouse is kaput," and "flying baker" (a navy reference to the signal flag for *B*, which is red and which signals "Beware, keep off").

Although most expressions, especially American ones, have a certain crude ingenuity, they are rarely positive. They seem intended either to hide the subject entirely (to some minds, the word is as shameful as the thing it signifies) or to defend against embarrassment by being overtly gross. We were unable to discover any new, more positive expressions, but we hope the emerging feminist sensibility will do so. Perhaps, then, American English will have an equivalent for the lovely Japanese expression for a girl's first menstruation, "the year of the cleavage of the melon," or for the ancient Indian "flower growing in the house of the god of love."

Chapter 12

* * * * * * * * * * * * * * *

RED HUMOR:
THE MENSTRUAL JOKE

What does a man do when he's about to bed his ladylove and she tells him she has "the curse"? If he's like Tina's lover in Sue Kaufman's *Diary of a Mad Housewife* (1968), he may say, "I don't mind that," and go ahead with his plans. If, however, he observes the common taboo on intercourse during menstruation, he may relieve his frustration with a joke.

Those who hold power are those who decide what is serious and what is a worthy target for a joke, a form of subtle verbal aggression. Usually, the target of the joke will be someone who is other than those in charge: Pole, black, homosexual, woman. And the jokes are often directed against what makes the target unavoidably different from the jokester; in a woman, her anatomy. Compared with jokes about breasts, vagina, and posterior, menstruation is a minor and less common subject. Yet, with the exception of puns, menstrual jokes almost invariably reveal male hostility toward women and their periods.

The pun is the most innocuous form of menstrual humor. The joke turns on words rather than on the deep-seated feelings other kinds of jokes seem to mask or displace. The word *menstruate* provides the basis for some of the wry word play. There is, for instance, the cockeyed seamstress. What was her problem? She couldn't "mend straight." [1] There's also the young woman whose boyfriend brags, "I have a Honda." She retorts, "I have my menstrual cycle." Both these jokes have little or nothing to do with the physical fact of menstruation.

A little closer to bodily reality is the remark in *Still More from Sex to Sexty:* "They're always talking about the Little Red School House back in the country . . . but you'd be red, too, if you had eight periods a day!" There's also the tale of the two unusual vampires: "They sat around chewing the rag." Still, unlike most menstrual jokes, these make no judgment on the menstruating woman.

Two jokes that are really aural puns turn on the lack of a period as a sign of pregnancy. In one, the joke teller's audience is asked why the sentence "Sister Mr." struck terror into the hearts of priests. The audience is expected to read the sentence as punctuated, making it read "Sister missed her [mister] period." We are not told the sentence's effect on the sister, only on the priests.

In a similar joke, the audience is asked to punctuate this group of words: Fun fun fun worry worry worry. The correct answer is: "Fun period fun period fun no period worry worry worry!"

The aim of puns is to demonstrate the verbal dexterity of the teller, not embarrass the listener. Most menstrual jokes, however, provide examples of the two purposes Freud saw in noninnocent jokes: to be hostile (aggressive, satirical, defensive) and to be obscene (exposing or denuding another, usually a woman). These jokes may further be classified as "smut," which according to Freud is "the intentional bringing into prominence of sexual facts and relations by speech." [2]

Hostility toward women appears most openly in jokes about the intercourse taboo, the idea that a woman should not engage in genital relations during menstruation ("¾ jazz time, ¼ ragtime"). In jokes, the woman's condition is almost invariably regarded from the man's point of view: as his defeat. For instance:

> A drugstore clerk who is given a black eye by a customer explains that he was only trying to make a companion sale. The

customer asked for a box of Kotex for his wife, and the clerk suggested, as a companion sale, "a deck of cards for a dull weekend!"

Obviously, the clerk assumed that the customer followed the intercourse taboo and that the customer needed another form of play to assuage sexual defeat. The customer preferred not to be reminded of his loss.

Another joke combines two all-American pastimes: football and bragging about sex.

Three football players decided to get married on the same day and to spend the wedding night at the same motel. They had worked out signals in advance: At the moment of climax, the players were to yell, "Touchdown!"

The big night finally arrived. From the star quarterback's room, after five minutes, came the yell, "Touchdown!" Five minutes later, the all-state tackle yelled, "Touchdown!"

In the center's room, all was silent. Finally, the other two players heard the center muttering, "Game postponed. Muddy field."

The farmer's daughters pretend to have their periods in order to avoid the salesman in one version of that perennial series of jokes. Staying overnight at the farmer's house, the salesman tries to climb into bed with the eldest daughter, who has put red ink on the sheets. Deflated, the amorous salesman moves from her (presumably) bloody bed to that of the second daughter, who performs the same trick. Feeling even smaller, the salesman finally gets to the bed of the youngest daughter and finds *green* ink on the sheets. Realizing the trick that's been played on him, the salesman asks why *green* ink. The young girl responds, "Because I'm not ripe yet."

Still another defeated lover is the man who "got Mary Lou as high as a kite, in the mood, and spread abed, but then he discovered there was a string attached to it."

In these jokes, the woman is seen in a passive or asexual role. She has to be sexually aroused by the man because she lacks the natural desires he has; she would rather pour ink than make love. The jokes correspond well with the Western classification of woman into two categories: the lady, the chaste woman to whom sex is distasteful, and the tramp, the bad woman who revels in sex. Both are defined with respect to men's view of them: The lady becomes a man's passive wife and mother; the tramp, his active mistress or prostitute.

Jokes may be directed against both kinds of women. A passive woman tells her story in a parody to the tune of "Bye Bye Blackbird." She is a young girl whose boyfriend taught her not to be a lady: to stop wearing underwear and to begin to "shake that thing." But romance died when

> You took me to a cottage in the wildwood,
> There you took advantage of my childhood.
> Put your hand beneath my dress,
> There you found a redbird's nest.
> Boyfriend, bye-bye.

We have found only one intercourse taboo joke in which a woman is active. Of course, she is a tramp. "One night all the gals in Hattie's Cat Flat were sick at the same time, so Madame Hattie decided to put on a menstrual show." The joke turns both on a pun and on the intercourse taboo but at least provides the woman with more than a passive role in men's eyes.

Obscenity (in Freud's sense) appears in jokes about the paraphernalia women must use during their periods. In these jokes, women are portrayed as somewhat unpleasantly tied to their physical processes.

One jingle advises a girl to remedy her problem:

> Rosie's is red,
> Her two lips are, too.
> Try Tampax, Rosie,
> That's what to do.

A riddle indicates the loathing with which female smells are regarded: "Why doesn't an elephant use a Tampax? If the average girl had to change them with her nose, she wouldn't either!" Every woman knows how fearful she is about spots and smells during her period. In the presence of these jokes, she is more likely to feel exposed and embarrassed than amused. Clearly, she is the butt of the joke, and her discomfiture can contribute to man's pleasure.

A 1946 nightclub act in Florida is said to have brought

down the house. In the performance, as recounted by G. Legman,

> The master of ceremonies' stooge pretends that he is drunk and confides that there is a slot machine in the ladies toilet.
>
> "Sure, there is," he insists when the master of ceremonies disagrees. "Where do you think I got this collar for my tux?" (Pulls out a woman's Kotex pad and hangs it around his neck, bringing down the house. Then as topper:) "Well, maybe it isn't a collar. I could use it as a simonizing rag for my car, except for these two pins." (Dangles the pad and belt-pins before the audience.) "I only went for cigarettes anyway." [3]

It is difficult to say what the audience found so amusing in this act. It may have been the association of a man with a female article of dress; men dressed in women's clothes have long been regarded as comical, as have whites in blackface. When those who control society ape their social inferiors, it is considered humorous, a voluntary—and only temporary—relinquishing of power.

The nightclub comedian was not alone in using the paraphernalia of menstruation in a supposed comic manner. Such joking has been used elsewhere as a form of obscenity against particular men, exposing and disparaging them by linking them to female objects. The famous country singer Tex Ritter was once reportedly silenced by a man who cracked, "Where's your Kotex?" ("coat, Tex"), implying that the star was weak, "effeminate."

A man in another joke pointedly rejects the association with female paraphernalia, even to the point of irrelevance.

> Noticing a man smoking on the bus, the driver turned around to him and asked, "Didn't you see the No Smoking sign?"
>
> The passenger replied, "Yeah, it's right below the one that says, Use Our Tampons. I didn't pay any attention to that one, either."

Peculiar associations between menstrual paraphernalia, scatology, and sexuality appear in this anecdote:

> Having a great need, Mr. Turdington Thudd found the men's room locked, so dashed in and occupied the ladies' room. Then

he noticed a bunch of fancy buttons on the wall by the commode. Foolishly, he pushed one, blacked out, and awoke in the hospital.

"Which button did you push?" he was asked. "The ATR button."

"That explains it. *That* button was the Automatic Tampax Remover!"

The diminution of the man to a lesser being is assumed. A real he-man controls his bowels, never uses the ladies' room or manifests undue curiosity, a stereotypical female trait.

A menstrual joke recounted in Marilyn Coffey's recent novel *Marcella* turns on another allegedly female trait: cattiness. Three society matrons were "sipping their tea with little fingers curled, and bragging about who was the daintiest."

> "I have such tiny feet," said the first. "Only size three. I can't get shoes small enough to fit me anywhere."
>
> "With me it's my hands," said the second. "My hands are so small I have to have my gloves 'specially made."
>
> The third lady excused herself, and went to the bathroom. When she came back, she said, "Oh, sorry to bother you, but do either of you have a Band-Aid? My period started." [4]

Menstrual bleeding itself, like paraphernalia, is used in jokes as a sign of women's inferiority. In one anecdote, the moron is told to ask his blind date "How about it?" She answers, "Not tonight. I have the rag on." He doesn't understand. "You know. I'm bleeding." He's still uncomprehending. She shows him. He answers, "Gee, no wonder you're all bloody. They cut your dick off." The joke defines woman as an incomplete man.

Homosexual men are also seen as incomplete males in many jokes. In one menstrual joke, two lovers are chatting together, and one gets a nosebleed. He cries to the other, "I'm bleeding! I'm bleeding!" His lover responds, "Thank God it came!" Like many other homosexual jokes, it seems to reveal the teller's anxiety about his own maleness.

Perhaps menstruation jokes are no more critical of women than many other kinds of jokes, such as women-driver jokes are. But the driver jokes disparage a certain *class* of women: those who drive. Menstrual jokes degrade women as a *caste:*

All women menstruate for a large part of their lives, and there is thus no way they can escape the ridicule and insult directed at them by this kind of humor.

One would like to think that feminism will help women develop a different sense of humor, one that is warm, loving, egalitarian, compassionate. But the one menstrual joke that seems to amuse women and men equally is the most perverse one. It combines punning, paraphernalia, and peculiarly American varieties of ethnic stereotype. Perhaps the black (or red) humor lies in the democracy of it all; unlike the jokes having women as the sole victims, this one spares hardly anyone.

> A black man was walking down a street and kicked a can. A Jewish genie arose from it in a cloud of smoke and said, "Okay, to you I'll give two wishes!"
>
> Delighted, the black man quickly announced his choices: "First, I want to be white; and then, I want to be surrounded by pussy." Immediately, he found himself transformed into—a tampon.
>
> The moral of the story: Never take anything from a Jew. It always comes with a string attached.

Chapter 13

. . . .

PERIODIC PARADE: MENSTRUATION IN ADVERTISING

Del Jordan feared well-groomed girls, for "never, never would they feel that little extra gush of blood, little bonus that no Kotex is going to hold, that will trickle horrifyingly down the inside of their thighs. No indeed; their periods would be discreet; nature served and did not betray them." Del, the protagonist in Alice Munro's *Lives of Girls and Women*,[1] fears exactly the kinds of girls who appear today in menstrual paraphernalia ads: ones who are always "confident," "safe," "secure," even during "those difficult times of the month."

The advertising image of the menstruating woman has shifted at times in response to national needs and ideology, for example, according to whether women are wanted in the home or in the war plant. Recent ads have become much more explicit and have moved from women's magazines onto television. Yet, the underlying message has been fairly consistent, playing on both hopes and fears: hopes that the woman will not have to change her ordinary life too much during "that time of the month"; fears (like Del Jordan's) of betrayal by dripping blood, revealing outlines, or odors.

Kotex "sanitary napkins" were invented at the end of the First World War and appeared on the market in 1921. Women who could afford them quickly substituted them for their "diapers," which usually had been washed and reused each month. But women's magazines did not immediately advertise the new products. Although *Ladies' Home Journal* carried an ad for "Amolin—the Personal Deodorant Powder" for women's "intimate personal uses," as early as 1920, there were no ads for napkins.[2] *Good Housekeeping* carried ads promoting Lysol for "every purpose of personal hygiene"[3] but did not advertise Kotex. Questions of discretion and/or prudery seem to have been involved.

By the 1930s, however, Kotex had penetrated *Good Housekeeping*. It took four years to convince *Ladies' Home Journal* to run the ads. In a 1933 *Good Housekeeping* ad, a woman in a shadow advertised "the new Phantom Kotex . . . no revealing outlines."[4] The new Phantom Kotex, still low priced, had "the same thickness, the same protective area," but the tapered ends helped "eliminate those tell-tale outlines." The ad's language stresses the hush-hush nature of menstruation: The pad must not be outlined; it must be "protective." No one must know the woman's guilty secret. Menstruation in the 1930s was, as it is today, a subject for concealment and euphemism, yet one for which "new" products must constantly be created.

In the 1940s, menstrual paraphernalia advertisers participated in the war effort. Because women's labor was needed, women were taken more seriously than they would be in later advertising. Ads called them women (i.e., adults), rather than girls; the language stressed utility and purpose and the ability of women to assume responsible and competent positions. Women were used to advise other women.

The ads for Lotus De Luxe "New Air-I-Ated Flow Napkin"[5] show a nurse speaking about the product; Meds goes farther, showing an absorbent tampon "perfected by a woman's doctor," who is also pictured.[6] San-Nap-Pak ads emphasize saving time and money: "No time to mince words— less time out for changes!"[7] The product reportedly gave "hours of extra service . . . without extra bulk!" To the extent that bulkiness is a physical, not a psychological, problem, the ad is a practical one; it meets a serious physical need for comfort without trying to create psychological tension.

Fibs ads from 1943 show women doing secretarial work, getting dressed for work, and wearing slacks, carrying a lunch-box, and punching a time card. Tampax ads stress that the product is "not limited to 'special' users. Many swimmers, bikers and movie stars have adopted Tampax, but it is de-signed every bit as much for the less strenuous woman at home or in the office."

A laudable feature of this ad, and most menstrual ads, is the absence of competition among women. Whereas most ad-vertising appeals to one's desire to "be the first on your block" and "get ahead of the gang," ads for menstrual products gener-ally do not draw lines between women. In this respect, mod-ern advertising has not changed from that of decades ago.

A wartime Kotex ad stresses the need for cooperation. A teen-aged girl sits brooding, her broom and mop in front of her, apparently having deserted the household tasks because she has her period. The ad chides,

> Who would have thought you'd turn out to be a deserter from a dustmop and a few dishes . . . when Mom's counting on you? When your *country's* counting on you? As Mom explained—it's girls like you taking on "homework" who release *a whole army of mothers* for rolling bandages and selling war bonds and driv-ing drill presses! [8]

The 1940s ads glorify bravery and competence, the qualities needed by women on the home front.

Betty Friedan has noted the remarkable changes in the contents of women's magazines after World War II.[9] Once, the woman who combined career and marriage, who worked hard for her country as well as her man, had been praised. But in the late 1940s and throughout the 1950s, the "feminine mys-tique" prevailed: the postwar idea that a woman's primary and only fulfilling roles were those of wife and mother, her place in the home. The men who ran women's magazines decided that women were now to be directed away from the factory and back into the home. Friedan documents the change in national ideology from the 1940s to the 1950s in magazine articles; a similar change can be seen in menstrual products ads.

Women's faces, without bodies, are shown more fre-quently in the 1950s than they were in the 1940s; to show a woman working is no longer important. Women are more often called "girls," indicating that the adult female is no longer taken so seriously. Instead of useful arguments, the advertisers use coy language arranged in short sentences. When women are less needed in the work force, their IQ automatically decreases, if we are to judge by advertisers' practices.

A typical example is a Tampax ad showing four women's faces.[10] All of them say, "We all use Tampax, of course." Each gives her reason: "Such a big difference! . . . So ingenious. . . . Daintiness plus. . . . Gives me confidence." The hardworking woman of the 1940s was not worried about daintiness and ingenuity; she sought a useful product enabling her to carry on needed chores.

The more ornamental view of women also appears in the 1953 Kotex ad.[11] Ten years after exhorting young girls to do the housework so their mothers could drive drill presses, the Kotex advertisers show an impeccably dressed mannequinlike woman standing in front of an art gallery. "Not a shadow of a doubt with Kotex," says the text. Kotex is soft, "dainty," with no outlines. In the corner of the page is a description of the woman's Herbert Sondheim dress, made in a "soft silk twill of tiny geometrics." The woman obviously does no useful work; a lady of leisure, she gazes and poses.

Also influencing the women of the 1950s were the "Modess, because . . ." ads, showing elegant, perfectly dressed models, often in voluminous swirls of lush fabric. The expression dated from a 1943 nationwide contest offering $25,000 in prizes for the best twenty-five-words-or-less completion of the sentence "I'm glad I switched to Modess because. . ." In 1949, the Modess—Because ads were named the best national ads of the year. They were so attractive that Del Jordan's boyfriend in *Lives of Girls and Women* used them as pinups; along with movie stars' pictures, he had "ladies in lovely ethereal dresses advertising sanitary napkins."

The woman of the 1940s bore burdens; in the 1950s, her burden was to be beautiful. A narrowing of woman's sphere came in every respect in that decade, as Friedan shows. In menstrual product ads, the woman's aspirations became individual and inner-directed (sleekness, beauty) rather than collective and outer-directed (the war effort). Even as late as 1970, the feminine mystique was not dead; a Kotex ad instructed women to "Be his. Be home. Be hard to forget. But be sure. Sure as Kotex napkins." [12]

In the ads of the 1960s and early 1970s, menstruation is still usually discussed with euphemisms: "those special days," "those difficult days," "that time of the month." "Special" is double-edged, used to imply both "noteworthy" and "problematic." One of the noteworthy or "special" problems is that women are not supposed to be able to talk directly about their periods. Unless they use Tampax, they may be forced into embarrassed excuses: "Tampax Tampons. So you won't have to make excuses. You're free to enjoy the magical water world. Anytime. No need to make excuses. Like 'I have this bad cold.' Or 'I have this awful hangnail.' " [13] Equally covert is the treatment of what to do with used menstrual paraphernalia. "Now—one more thing *not* to worry about . . . that little discussed disposal problem. Now—neat, discreet, disposal bags come in each box of new Scott Confidets." [14] Menstruating women should be embarrassed, say advertisers.

Even those ads that promote their products with a more positive tone tend to stress psychology over technology. For instance, the word *absorbent* appears far less frequently than the terms *secure, confident,* and *free.* Sometimes, advertisers seem to suffer from a poverty of vocabulary: "The way you feel is free. Today and everyday, you feel free, confident, unhampered. Tampax tampons worn internally make this possible. Keep you feeling good and comfortably confident, in or out of the water . . . for total freedom, total comfort . . . Tampax." [15]

In the last decade, the pictures accompanying menstrual ads are usually of young women, no older than twenty-five. They are more active than in the 1950s, although their activity is usually a sport (swimming, tennis playing) rather than gainful employment. Except for ads in black magazines, the women are usually white. Even when the model's color changes, the ads are exactly the same—same layout, same text. The women are all smiling, well-groomed, confident—the kind Del Jordan feared.

Within the last few years, however, there have been

some changes in the advertising. In line with the general cultural trend toward the natural look and natural foods, recent ads have begun to substitute *natural* for words like *confident* and *free*. For instance, Kotex tampons "are a lot like you. Soft and natural. Soft, natural shape. Natural insertion guides instead of bulky tubes." [16]

There is also greater explicitness in advertising, perhaps in recognition of the sexual revolution. Ads for tampons now say "young girls" more frequently than they say "unmarried girls" when discussing the tampon's effect on a hymen. Pursettes, which used to call itself "the tampon that's right even for single girls," now advertises itself as "the comfort tampon."

In recent years, a new product has appeared on the menstrual market. Tassaway is a small, soft cup used to collect menstrual blood. Its ads are factual and appeal to the intelligence, using the terms *menses* and *uterus*.[17] Whereas other ads say coyly that there's "nothing hard" about insertion, Tassaway is more positive and less authoritative, quoting a satisfied customer: "Once you get the 'feel' of it you can't go wrong." Tassaway ads also say "women" rather than "girls"; the ad's sentences are longer and more complex. The Tassaway ad shows a respect for women's minds and points to a direction in which ads for menstrual products might go.

Very recent magazine ads, probably influenced by the women's movement, have returned to the 1940s practice of showing women at work. A Tampax ad stresses

> on-the-job security. It's your job and you love it. It's hectic—it's hard work—it's a ball! But no matter how busy you are, you always feel in charge, confident, calm. Even it it's the wrong time of the month. . . . And that's important when your job means more to you than just a paycheck.[18]

No doubt because menstruation is considered a taboo subject, the product itself is shown much less frequently than a woman is. Although Pursettes tampons were introduced to women in 1955, an unwrapped tampon was not shown until 1968.[19] Pursettes ads in late 1973 show a size comparison between a Pursette and a lipstick. Other advertisers are still keeping their products under wraps and in a box.

Although television and sanitary napkins are about the same age, until November 1, 1972, ads for sanitary protection products were banned from TV and radio. Tassaway worked hard to break the ban, for without the electronic media, it had no sure way to inform and educate women about the product. By running ads on stations that do not subscribe to the code of the National Association of Broadcasters, with little adverse public reaction, they eventually helped convince the NAB to lift the ban. Scott's Confidets also tested ads on noncode stations and was the first menstrual hygiene product to receive code authority for a television commercial. Modess was first on radio and is now also on television. Interestingly, Kimberly-Clark fought the lifting of the television ban, claiming the products "too personal," but now uses the medium for competitive purposes. Perhaps they didn't want any new information that might spoil Kotex's impressive share of the market to reach the consumer.

Of course, the companies are restricted in what they can say on the air and when they can say it. The ads may make no reference to absorbency, cleanliness, anatomy, comfort, insertion, application, duration of efficacy. This leaves "generalized statements relating to grooming, femininity, freshness" and "statements related to supplemental aspects of a product and general product description" such as packaging and disposability, and the like.[20] Perhaps this latest directive is responsible for the disposal bags, towelettes, and other gimmicks. The ads are usually shown during "women's hours" (daytime television) or late-night programming, when the children are in bed.

A good example of the kind of thinking that animates these restrictions is shown by the remark of a Kimberly-Clark executive. "Menstrual care is such a very personal thing to a woman," he said. "For example, she equates changing her brand of tampons almost with committing adultery." [21] No such Neanderthal thinking obscures advertising in Europe. We have been told of a German television commercial for O-B Tampons in which a stewardess's skirt is snatched from her by an overeager passenger. In the flash of fabric and fadeout are heard the words: "I'm glad I'm wearing my O-B Tampon!"

Chapter 14

RAGS TO RICHES:
THE MENSTRUAL PRODUCTS
INDUSTRY

We do not know what Eve wore as sanitary protection after she was "cursed." European artists often show her wearing a fig leaf, not a very absorbent material. We are told that in some cultures women wear no protection and have few taboos; [1] whereas in our own society, there are now approximately fifty different brand-name napkins and tampons, and "feminine products" is a half-billion-dollar industry.

Through the ages, women have used either tampons or bandages as sanitary protection. But until World War I, the only significant improvement over the basic bandage was that the "civilized" matrons of the Roman Empire used cloth bandages; whereas their "savage" sisters in Africa and Australia used bandages made of grass or vegetable fiber.[2] Thrifty Frenchwomen were still washing out their menstrual rags in the 1940s; in parts of South America, disposable napkins are only now being mass marketed.

Among tampon users, there was more variety. In ancient Japan, women used from eight to twelve paper tampons a day, held in place by a bandage called *kama* ("pony"). For centuries, Indonesian women made tampons from vegetable fiber. Roman women wore tampons of soft wool; and Egyptian women, rolls of soft papyrus. Rolls of grass and roots served women in Equatorial Africa.[3]

Until about 1925, American women wore a diaper of bird's-eye or outing flannel, which they were obliged to wash and reuse. These were cumbersome, uncomfortable, and apt to cause soreness. Johnson and Johnson manufactured "Lister's Towels" in 1896, the first commercial disposable pad, made of gauze-covered cotton. But because turn-of-the-century morality prevented advertising these "unmentionables," the pads did not reach many women and were eventually withdrawn from the market.

Then, during the First World War, French nurses discovered that the cellulose material used for bandaging wounds absorbed menstrual blood better than cloth diapers. In 1921, Kimberly-Clark made the first successful disposable sanitary napkin, Kotex, which, like the same company's Kleenex, has become a generic name. Johnson and Johnson returned to the market in 1927 with Modess, manufactured by its subsidiary, the Personal Products Company. Kotex and Modess had the field more or less to themselves until 1961, when Scott Paper Company came out with Confidets. Today, Kotex products command approximately a 55 percent share of the total napkin market, Modess reaches about 35 percent, and Confidets is in third place with 10 to 11 percent.

Between 1921 and today, the sanitary napkin has undergone constant improvement, but the basic design remained the same until the advent of Stayfree Mini-pads, a Personal Products innovation, in 1970. These smaller pads, designed to be fastened to panties with a thin strip of adhesive, found a ready audience. Fan letters (which we have seen) extolled their use for everything from bladder problems and vaginal discharge to emergency lifts inside a pair of shoes. One writer went so far as to say the pads "almost make me wish I weren't ready for menopause!" Kotex is now in this zooming market with New Freedom Small Pads and Lite-Days Oval Pads, and both Kotex and Modess have regular-size pads with the strip of adhesive, for "beltless freedom."

The ecology movement spawned a school of "flushable" products, another innovation on the basic napkin. Stayfree

Maxi-pads and Modess Flush-able claim to be both flushable *and* biodegradable. As one researcher explained to us, you can flush even a steel ball down the toilet; the key to an ecologically responsible product that won't create a tornado in the plumbing is biodegradability.

Tampons are not biodegradable, but in most households, they are eminently flushable. Disposable tampons have been on the market in the United States since the invention of Tampax in 1933, but from the myths, misconceptions, and dark mutterings about spoiled virginity, you would think they had sprung full-blown from the forehead of Jack the Ripper. When they were first introduced, even the churches got into the act, in a rare show of concern for women's bodies, and disputed for some years over the tampon as an engine of contraception, masturbation, or defloration (even though the napkin, with its constant pressure on the clitoris, is a more likely candidate for devil's disciple). Happily, all now agree on the product's harmlessness, and tampons are fast overtaking napkins, with an average 12 percent growth over the past five years (although the majority of women still use pads exclusively).

As might be expected, Tampax has the lioness's share of the tampon market and is the largest advertiser. Playtex is number two; Kotex tampons, three. The tube-applicator tampon is favored by 80 percent of all tampon users, for reasons probably having to do with our Puritan heritage. In Europe, however (where the major U.S. manufacturers have factories and subsidiary companies), applicatorless tampons do extremely well.

In 1969, the Tassette Company of California introduced the first truly new menstrual product since the fig leaf. A plastic cup that looks like an upside-down Liberty Bell, the Tassaway, when properly folded, fits into the vagina and collects the flow. Because there is no absorption, there is no leakage; because it can hold more volume than the average tampon, the danger of overflow is minimal; because it is made of plastic, no bacteria can grow on it. Some women find the Tassaway uncomfortable; others find it messy to remove. Although the company's literature says otherwise, it can be used more than once. But most women dispose of the Tassaway immediately after emptying it, which makes the package scarcely "the equivalent of 25 to 30 tampons or napkins," as advertised on the box.

The most advanced development in monthly protection, still in its experimental stage, is period extraction: the removal of the entire flow at once by inserting a suction tube (cannula) into the uterus. This "fifteen-minute period," when perfected, could be the most efficient method of dealing with the menstrual period; but right now, the risks of infection or tissue damage are high. Changing attitudes toward fertility and a reluctance to accept "woman's lot" in all areas of life would seem to make this technique a logical next step.

In their journey from rags to riches, the manufacturers have relied heavily on gimmickry to liven up sales. The huge success of vaginal deodorant sprays (the manufacturers first created the need and then rushed to fill it) inspired napkin and tampon makers to capitalize on the odor mania and "deodorize" their products. What passes for deodorant in most napkins is, of course, perfume. The exception to this is the Modess napkin-with-deodorant-protection. The gridlike construction of the napkin (similar to that of Kotex Plus, which also incorporates a small extra napkin within the larger) spreads the flow over a larger internal area, with the surface remaining drier and therefore less odorous because the menstrual flow develops an odor only when it hits the air.

But that fact makes the deodorized tampon a useless innovation—and an example of just how gullible the public can be. The Food and Drug Administration has already begun receiving reports that question the safety of these products,[4] but as in the case of the sprays, such reports will probably have no effect on their success or failure in the marketplace.

Other gimmicks include individual disposal bags (Confidets) and, most recently, "towelettes" in boxes of Kimberly-Clark's Fems.

One other method of sanitary protection remains to be mentioned: the household sponge. Following the advice of Alicia Bay Laurel in *Living on the Earth*,[5] we made our own tampons out of a sponge. One 12-cent O-Cel-O kitchen sponge (3½ by 4¾ inches) divided widthwise into four equal strips makes four perfect tampons. One sponge, we found, lasted for as long as 6¼ hours during a heavy flow, as opposed to only 4 hours with a Pursettes Plus. The sponge is economical and, if it is sterilized by boiling, reusable. It is by far the best protection *not* on the market, but it would probably not find overwhelming favor with the millions of women brainwashed by the manufacturers to "change often" to ensure "daintiness."

THE INDUSTRY

Retail sales of feminine hygiene products exceed $500 million annually. Vaginal sprays and certain birth control products pad the figures somewhat, so it is not a completely accurate representation of sales of *menstrual* products. But it does give some indication of the size of the market.

We wanted to get the most complete picture possible of the sanitary products industry, so we visited the Personal Products Company in Milltown, New Jersey. We chose this company purely for reasons of time and distance; to avoid bias, however, we wrote to every other manufacturer in the country, seeking information on the history of the company, product testing research, finances, advertising, and other details relevant to the individual companies. Tassaway, Kimberly-Clark, Tampax, and the Campana Corporation (Pursettes) responded.[6]

Making the Products

Tampons and sanitary napkins are made from rayon and wood pulp. The more compressible rayon is used for tampons; the wood pulp, which is more absorbent but noncompressible, is used in napkins.

No federal agency governs product specifications in the sanitary products industry, nor are there industry-wide boards of standards. "House" brand napkins and tampons, for example, which are usually *not* made by the major manufacturers, may be cheaper than the name brands, but they are also of lower quality. The government monitoring of advertising claims is the only official pressure applied to the companies, but the response of the public is a steadily effective deterrent to the production of shoddy goods. At Personal Products, both salaried and wage employees participate in quality control. Explicit product specifications are followed along the route from tree to container, and there are several in-process checks of the napkins and tampons at the machine, the packing table, and the shipping platform. Such items as quality of adhesive, length of tabs, and compactness of fibers are checked, and the threat of pay loss is a further incentive to employees at all levels to produce quality products. In the positive-reinforcement department, plant employees see the complimentary letters from satisfied users of their product, attend screenings of the company's educational films, and are made to realize that they have a stake in the company's success.

Research and Education

Although its products have the world's largest captive audience, the industry gave us a pleasant surprise at the amount of money it spends on product improvement and education of the public. Ingenious contraptions are used at Personal Products constantly to test the rate of absorption and fluid capacity of products from all manufacturers in simulated use situations, and a group of women test the products themselves under the supervision of a doctor. In both cases, the used napkins and tampons are carefully studied for fluid patterns and amount of fluid retained. Both Personal Products and Campana Corporation, which were the only companies to give us detailed information on their test methods and procedures, claim test results showing the superiority of their own products over other brands. We were convinced of the honesty of the testing and the sincerity of their claims, and we urge readers to look more closely at certain tampon ads. Because of the shape of the vagina, tampons that expand in width, such as Pursettes and Carefree, are more likely to give better protection, as the ads say, than tampons that expand only in length, such as Tampax.

Tampax supplied us with an impressive set of medical studies, dating from 1945 through the late 1960s, proving the safety of the tampon. Despite the fact that tampons are as old as civilization and had long been used for contraception and medication as well as for menstrual protection, they were suspected of causing such conditions as endometriosis, cervicitis, and vaginitis. A 1965 study by the Rock Reproductive Clinic found, however, that the "use of vaginal tampons has no physiological or clinical undesired side effects. This is true even when tampons are used in the presence of injury or inflammation." Another study tested the use of tampons after childbirth, beginning at ten days postpartum, and found no evidence of "increased vaginal irritation, or delay in healing of either episiotomy or the reproductive organs." (It must be said, though, that many women who have vaginitis or inflamed or irritated cervices do not use tampons because the tampons hurt.)

Similar tests preceded the introduction of Tassaway into the national market. The Tassaway had previously been used successfully to treat certain disorders of the bladder and reproductive organs. A 1963 study from the vulvovaginitis clinic of Mount Sinai Hospital found that the Tassaway prevented infection and odor and was comfortable to use.

The manufacturers of menstrual products for the most part serve their customers well. They supply a product for which a real need exists, and they look hard for ways to improve it. But in one serious way they fail.

The basic sanitary napkin is no better than menstrual protection used thousands and thousands of years ago. Absorbency, disposability, comfort do not change the basic design. The napkin is still a breeding ground for bacteria (not from the menstrual flow itself, which is bacteriologically "clean," but from the anal and urinary tracts, contributing to vaginal infections). In our hygiene-oriented society, it is amazing that such a product is so widely accepted. Nowhere does the literature from companies making both napkins and tampons attempt to dissuade women from continued use of the pad. Nor has any company yet made a tampon that a woman with a heavy flow can wear with complete security, so that she will not need even the mini-pad "just in case." Instead of adding disposal bags to an overcluttered world, these companies should be using their talents to develop new ways to deal with menstruation, whether menstrual extraction or some process as yet undreamed of. As long as the sanitary napkin is applied like a bandage to a wound, women cannot forget the cover-up approach to menstruation.

Chapter 15

. . . .

MENSTRUATION GOES PUBLIC

In the 1970s, a new explicitness is in the air; for the first time, menstruation appears openly in cartoons, in insults reported in the media. More positively, it becomes a subject for television, songs, and commercial movies.

The uses of menses-as-insult are not new; what is new is the public reporting of them—no more cover-up, no more "Modess, because . . ." The new menstrual insults appear in contexts both traditional and innovative. An article on pitcher Tom Seaver reports the standard clubhouse "ragging" (a pun?): "One player will pay attention to another by tying up his clothes or stuffing Tampax in his locker." [1] Athletes have always taunted one another with aspersions on the other's supposed (and dreaded) femininity; now, the paraphernalia of menstruation are used to make the same insult. Even transvestite singer Wayne County, himself dressing in feminine clothing, uses paraphernalia to insult men. Bothered by a ringside heckler, County once responded, "Go stuff a Kotex down your throat, you asshole!" [2]

Nor are paraphernalia insults aimed only at men. *Village Voice* columnist Jill Johnston tells of a "jock on the plane out of s.f." who was insulting a woman. Johnston became especially incensed because he'd "brandished a Kotex at this woman," and Johnston planned to "crack the guy on 'is head" with her *Mainliner Magazine*.[3]

But it is the iconoclastic *National Lampoon* that finally gives a man his comeuppance. A Spanish dandy serenades a mantilla-wearing lady on a balcony. Instead of a rose, she flings down to him a bloody tampon (colored red in an otherwise black-and-white cartoon).

Not all examples of the new openness are insulting or even negative. Although television, songs, and film may allude to the discomforts of menstruation, there are also instances of pleasure and celebration of being a woman.

TELEVISION

Jackie Gleason didn't think it should be done on television. Menstruate, that is. But the Great One was behind the times; 1973 was the year that the menses hit the tube.

All in the Family, TV's breaker of taboos, broke the menstrual barrier in an episode called "The Battle of the Month," first aired on March 24, 1973. Gloria is irritable because of her period and quarrels with her mother, Edith. Archie, conservative in all matters, objects to Gloria's talking about her period in front of him. Sally Struthers, the actress who plays Gloria, was allegedly the inspiration for this episode. According to one of the show's writers, "When Sally Struthers has her menstrual period, forget it. She can't work, she's headachy, she's irritable—we took it from her. And it worked." According to the writer, the "menstrual episode" was not done for shock value.[4]

But it did shock. It generated more mail than any other episode that season, most of it objecting to mentioning the menses. Viewers seemed to agree with Jackie Gleason, who argued in a *New York Times* interview that "there is nothing funny about a menstrual period . . . these are not suitable topics."[5]

All in the Family's sister show *Maude* treated periods in a more offhand, casual way. In an episode aired on January 29, 1974, Maude, her husband, Walter, and friends are marooned in an out-of-the-way railroad station during a blizzard. The intrepid Maude looks for a candy machine and reports to the group, "The one in the ladies' room works: you can have a Clark bar or a Midol." Walter advises, "Buy a Midol—we might be here all month." The target of his humor, such as it is, seems to be the weather rather than menstruation; his remark, then, demonstrates a healthy nonchalance toward women's periods.

Even better than nonchalance is a feeling of sisterhood among women because of menstruation. On *The Mary Tyler Moore Show*, September 29, 1973, Mary and her friend Rhoda reminisce about the trials of puberty. Rhoda finds one of her old diaries and reads, "Today my mother came into my room and whispered that something wonderful is going to happen to me—once a month." Her conversation with Mary is easily integrated with the rest of the story: Mary and Rhoda are in New York for the marriage of Rhoda's friend. Their adolescent memories provide a bond between them.

By now, many casual references to menstruation have been heard on a wide variety of programs. But to date, the most positive image of menstruation on television we've encountered is *I Love You, Goodbye*, a made-for-TV movie first shown on February 12, 1974. The central character, Karen Chandler (played by Hope Lange), leaves her insensitive husband and three children. She then meets a potential lover, Alex, but she ends the relationship when she breaks a date in order to be with her daughter Julie, who is having her first period. Karen tells Julie her future is bright, she has many choices ahead of her, and that's what women's liberation really means. It is a remarkable episode. Not only does a woman put another woman's needs ahead of a man's (a rare choice in literature, as in life), but they both celebrate the menstrual process, seeing it as a fulfillment, not as something to be hidden or denied.

SONGS

Menstruation is celebrated more often in story than in song. It is something to write home to your mother about but not something you sing about onstage. We have found very few songs mentioning the menses, and most are by men. The Rolling Stones seem to refer to it in their song "I Can't Get No Satisfaction" in which the girl says, "Baby, better come back, maybe next week." Does Bob Dylan refer to menstruation in "Just Like a Woman" when he writes these lines: "She aches just like a woman," and "your long time curse hurts"?

For Simon and Garfunkel in their "Big Bright Green Pleasure Machine," menstruation is one of a list of problems. Along with "Does your group have more cavities than theirs?" comes the line: "Are you worried 'cause your girlfriend's just a little late?"

These songs all treat menstruation as it impinges upon the male consciousness: as a sign of lack of pregnancy and as a reason for postponing sexual contact. New women artists can be expected to treat menstruation as women see it, and they are beginning to do so. At the first National Women's Music Festival, held in May 1974, a group called the Clinch Mountain Back-Steppers performed a song called "The Bloods" by Debbie Lempke. Funny and frank, the song acknowledges, "Some sisters get down for menstruation / Ain't no time for sad desperation." As if in response to the male songwriters' view, the third stanza asserts:

> Men keep sayin' that the bloods are bad
> Because it means you ain't fertile
> That you ain't been had

The refrain joyously proclaims the renewal of body and spirit that can be possible when a woman embraces the "natural rhythm" of her body:

> There's a new day comin'
> When you got the bloods again.[6]

FILMS

The treatment of menstruation in film has followed a path similar to that of television. First, there is the groundbreaking: the mention of the periods, perhaps to shock, ultimately to be nonchalant. Then, there is the probing into women's thoughts about menstruation, positive or negative. And finally, there is celebration of the monthly bleeding as part of the pleasure of being a woman.

In 1973 and 1974, mention of menstruation, previously rare, became common. Most references, both in earlier and in later films, were of the usual kind: missed periods and fears of pregnancy (*Images, Travels with My Aunt, Saturday Night and Sunday Morning, The Lords of Flatbush*), the intercourse taboo during menstruation (*McCabe and Mrs. Miller, Diary of a Mad Housewife*), women's unhappiness with cramps (*They Shoot Horses, Don't They; Rosemary's Baby*). But two fairly recent foreign films make menstruation, for the first time, a central event in film, one treated not only verbally but also visually.

In Ingmar Bergman's *Cries and Whispers*, Ingrid Thulin plays a wife who feels great antagonism toward her husband. In order to avoid having sexual relations with him, she takes a broken wine glass to her genitals, and the blood rushes out from between her legs in a false menstruation. Smiling fiercely, as if achieving an orgasm through pain, she smears some of the blood on her face.

The scene is difficult to interpret. Is it menstruating that is loathsome, or self-mutilation? Is Bergman sympathizing with or humiliating his female character? The sequence, in any interpretation, is an unforgettable one, and the red of the blood is linked visually with other reds in the film, as in the red-outs, rather than blackouts, sometimes used to end scenes. Bergman is perhaps the first director to use menstrual red for its color, as beauty, in the ways that other directors have used the red blood of killings and woundings (compare, for example, *A Clockwork Orange*). Bergman's scene is an affirmation of the color potential of menstrual blood but hardly a celebration of its meaning for a woman.

The celebration *is* present in *Valerie and Her Week of Wonders*, a Czech film written by Ester Krumbachova and Jaromil Jires and directed by Jires. The film was shown in New York and at the Chicago and San Francisco film festivals in 1972 and 1974. Valerie is a thirteen-year-old girl entering puberty. Her first period leads to a week of wonderful sexual awakening in which imagination runs into riotous fantasy.

Discovering that "she is no longer a child," she imagines tooth-chomping vampires, lewd priests seducing wholesome virgins, weasels doing vanishing acts; plagues and murders occur. Lyrical music and surreal images flow together; the line between fantasy and reality is never entirely clear. There are even magic earrings, shaped like little silver bells, with "pearls" (perhaps a clitoral symbol) inside them, that save their owner from many dangers: incest (the vampires are very loving toward one another), rape, neck bites, death at the stake, and an actual partridge in a pear tree.

In the end, the whole family lives in a sort of vampire Valhalla, leading the good life of happiness and sensuality. Valerie walks about, watching it all calmly, now a "blood" part of this society. *Valerie and Her Week of Wonders* consists of beautiful images, and it celebrates menstruation as a gateway, an awakening to the new perceptions and possibilities in being a woman. It is the first truly feminist film about the menarche. Certainly, there will be more.

Part Four

. . . .

MENSTRUAL IMAGES IN LITERATURE

. . . .

Chapter 16

THE BLEEDING TOWER: MENSTRUAL THEMES IN FAIRY TALES

Weaving in and out of the mythmaking imaginations of centuries are those symbols of the eternal feminine: blood, flowers, the witch, the moon. When these images appear in poetry, fiction, or mythology, critics are reluctant to associate them with that most female of attributes, the menstrual cycle. The same neglect has applied to the menstrual themes that seem to fill the universe of folktales. There is no mention of them in collections and codifications of folktale motifs.

Fairy tales told to children are built on ritual and myth, embellished with the narrative art. Because they occupy an intermediate position between true myth and high art, they show us human beings linking profound and unchanging myths about the meaning of life with the naïve wish fulfillment of storytelling. Studies of repeating themes and motifs in folktales throughout the Indo-European language group and beyond reveal these homely tales to be rooted in common experience, fears, and misconceptions. It is thus logical that the terror of menstrual blood, one of the most profound imprints on the collective unconscious, should occupy a prominent place in these tales.

Many of the menstrual themes and allusions in fairy tales are filtered through the character of the witch, a figure who appears in some form in most Western tales and who is closely associated with fear of menstruation. But certain key elements of plot also recall the practices of menarcheal seclusion and avoidance of the menstruating woman common to primitive societies and to many advanced societies as well. Thus, the young heroines of fairy tales are inevitably pubertal maidens who must undergo some trial before being allowed to live happily ever after with Prince Charming. Furthermore, the image patterns and repeated symbolic motifs rely heavily on the white-red-black color progression of the Great Goddess and on blood and flowers as essential components of plot development.

We shall limit ourselves here to some of the 200-plus *Household Tales* collected by the Brothers Grimm. They are familiar, and they are the stories most illustrative of our European-American heritage.[1]

THE FAIRY TALE WITCH

In *The Fear of Women,* Wolfgang Lederer points out that witches usually are either very old or very young. The old ones deal in "envy and malice"; and the young specialize in "love magic," concocting potions from their newly flowing menstrual blood.[2] The old witch in Grimms' tales has the appearance of the menopausal woman of old: protruding nose and chin, facial hair, bowed back, coarsened voice. She specializes in malicious curses on the young and frequently has in her care a pubertal maiden. More than once in the stories, she is associated with child cannibalism. Black is her color, the color of death, decay, and the crone aspect of the Great Goddess.

The young witch is almost never the heroine but is frequently the natural daughter of the old witch (the heroine is usually her stepdaughter). Following Lederer's description, the young witch is usually found plotting to steal the bridegroom from the true bride and frequently uses some magic arts learned from her mother to assist herself. Examples of the

young witch abound in Grimms' tales, but the most familiar
are Cinderella's stepsisters.

Lederer suggests that something about the child-rearing
function seems to dim both the white and the black magic of
witches; [3] thus, the age of a witch must be one extreme or the
other. We must emphasize further that at menarche and menopause the menstrual function is extremely influential in a
woman's life, informing her attitudes and personality. During
the childbearing years, however, menstruation is important
more for its usefulness as a guide to fertility—that is, when it
appears. Pregnancy and lactation combine to suppress menstruation for long periods of a woman's childbearing years.
Thus, even in folklore, the conclusion is that menstruation
causes a woman to act like a witch.

The Witch as Bad Mother

When a woman feels witchy, her menstrual period is at
fault, say some psychoanalysts. We discussed in Chapter 8
the ancient fear that a woman's "natural" feelings of destructiveness toward her children are intensified during her periods. Even worse, the mother of a pubescent daughter may
experience barely controllable rage as the daughter blossoms
and the mother decays. The dualism in the personality of the
mother is expressed in fairy tales in Western culture by two
mothers: the natural mother and the stepmother. The true
mother is good and loving but dies prematurely, frequently at
the birth of a longed-for daughter. The stepmother is wicked
and seeks to harm the child or shut her away from the world.

Snow White is blessed with just such a pair of mothers.
The true mother looks out a window and wishes for the birth
of a child; the stepmother looks into a mirror and wills the
death of the child. Arland Ussher, an Irish critic, has linked
these two mothers to Eve and Lilith, Adam's fertile and barren
wives, suggesting the archetype of all dual-mother roles in
these tales.[4]

In "Sweetheart Roland," the envious stepmother hates
the daughter's beauty and plots to cut off her head. She kills
her own child instead, and the drops of blood from the severed

head speak to her, suggesting that she is gaining self-knowledge from this "first bleeding" of the daughter. In "Brother and Sister" (also called "The Enchanted Stag"), the stepmother sends her stepchildren into the forest to die (as in "Hansel and Gretel"); when they survive, she then attempts to kill the stepdaughter and steal her child. Only the magical appearance of the real mother to nurse the baby defeats the witch's power (lactation suppressing menstruation).

The witches in "Snow White" and "Hansel and Gretel" are also devouring mothers, another problem for the analysts. Hansel and Gretel escape being roasted for dinner by Gretel's wits; Snow White's stepmother eats the lung and liver of a wild boar, thinking they are Snow White's.

Both the psychoanalytic theories of maternal destructiveness and the imagined crimes against children attributed to historical witches emerge in these children's fables. Both are tied in with the fear inspired by menstrual blood: the fear that the normal order of things can be reversed, and the life-creating womb become a bloody chamber of death.

CASTRATION ANXIETY

There is extensive fear among all peoples that witches and menstruating women are the archetypal castrating females. Various anthropological studies claim that the extensiveness of menstrual taboos in a society reflects that society's degree of castration anxiety. Church decrees against witches in the Middle Ages accused them directly of causing impotence. And castration anxiety inspired by menstrual blood finds latent expression in Grimm in the mutilation of young men as they try to overcome a witch's curse and reach a young woman who is under her influence. So, we find that Rapunzel's lover is blinded when the witch throws him from the tower, and that all princes who tried to penetrate the briar roses around Sleeping Beauty's castle before the hundred years were up perished.

Somewhat displaced castrations occur in "The Twelve Brothers" and "The Six Swans." In the first, the birth of a thirteenth child, a girl,[5] means that the twelve brothers must die. This is the first castration in the story. The brothers escape and set up house in the forest; when their sister, grown to puberty, reaches them, they live happily together until the girl plucks some flowers ("flowers" means menstruation in many cultures), an action that turns the brothers into ravens. In this nonhuman form, impotent to act as men, the brothers must remain for seven years. "The Six Swans" has a similar plot: Six brothers are turned into swans and can only be released by fulfillment of a trial of silence and work by their sister.

It is also possible to regard transformation stories such as "The Frog Prince" and "Snow White and Rose Red" as tales reflecting fear of castration by a menarcheal child. In both, a prince has been changed into an animal and is dependent on the unselfish love of a maiden to regain his human masculinity.

SECLUDED MAIDENS

The unseemly haste with which nubile maidens were locked away in towers in the land of Grimm seems to be a direct narrative analogue to the custom of seclusion at menarche in most early societies. As we described in Chapter 3, newly menstruating girls in Africa, the South Pacific, India, and the Americas were commonly separated from their tribes at their first menstruation, some for a few days, some for four or five years. The purpose of the seclusion was to protect the girl and her society from her mana at this dangerous time. Important during this seclusion were the instructions they received from the older women of the tribe in female matters. The natural mother, however, was almost universally excluded. At the end of the seclusion, the girls were considered marriageable and were welcomed into the adult life of the tribe.

Sleeping Beauty, Rapunzel, and Maid Maleen, to name a few, were kept from the eyes of the world during their adolescence and endured their seclusion at the behest of, or in the company of, a bad mother (a witch or other old person not their natural mother). In many stories of this type, a pointed reference is made to the age of the girl when her seclusion began: Sleeping Beauty was cursed at her birth by a fairy who said that on her fifteenth birthday, she would prick her finger on a spindle and die. Bleeding at fifteen seems an obvious reference to the menarche. Rapunzel was shut in her tower at age twelve, another menarcheal age, although she had lived with the witch from birth.

The places of seclusion were impenetrable. Everyone, even the flies on the wall, slept for 100 years in Sleeping Beauty's castle. Rapunzel's tower had no stairs and only one tiny window; like the sacred priests and kings, she was literally suspended between heaven and earth. Maid Maleen's tower didn't even have a window; she and a waiting woman were shut away when she refused to marry her father's choice. When her seven-year seclusion was up, she chipped away some stones and found that the land had been ravaged and only they had survived. Here is an example of the menarcheal seclusion protecting the girl herself from the dangers of her state.

SECLUSION AFTER MARRIAGE

The frequent trials imposed on married women involving separation, actual or symbolic, from their husbands, is a lesser-known aspect of many fairy tales. It suggests to us the representation in folklore of the taboo against intercourse with a menstruating woman.

For example, after the witch found out about Rapunzel's tower assignations with the prince, she took her into the wilderness and forced her to live in great hardship. It took seven years for the prince to find her, handicapped as he was by the blindness (castration) he suffered when he fell from the tower. But Rapunzel had an eye-opening surprise for him: seven-year-old twins born to her in the wild. This suggests not only the menstrual intercourse taboo, with its attendant fear of castration or impotence, but also the seclusion imposed on women after childbirth, all blood from the genitals being considered dangerous to men.

In both "The Twelve Brothers" and "The Six Swans," to release her brothers from a charm, a bride must keep silent for seven years, during which time she is married and bears children. In "The Pink," a queen is shut away in a tower that "neither the sun nor moon could penetrate" for seven years following the kidnapping of her newborn son and the false accusation that she had murdered him. The bride in "The Lady and the Lion" must follow her enchanted husband all over the world for seven years when he is changed into a dove; every seventh step, he sheds a drop of blood and a white feather so that she will be able to follow.

In "Fairy Tell True," a fourteen-year-old girl, told to look behind only twelve of thirteen doors in the palace of the good fairy she lives with, fails the test of obedience and is permanently stained with gold on her finger from the thirteenth room. The gold is suggestive of the permanent stain of menstrual blood, and the fairy recalls the witches and other non-maternal guardians of menarcheal girls. The child is sent into seclusion and struck dumb until she is willing to confess her transgression to the fairy. A king marries her, but she remains dumb through the early marriage and the birth of several children. This condition and the stain of gold suggest that she is expiating the stain of the menstrual blood and its evil connotations and keeping a tabooed distance from her husband as a prelude to living a normal life, just as the heroines of other stories underwent tests and trials to save their marriages from menstrual contamination.

COLORS

The Grimm tales are full of precise descriptions of appearance or action. Some descriptive emblems and motifs recur constantly and point to associations that go back to the mythic and ritualistic origins of the tales. One such recurring motif is the use of the colors white, red, and black.

Snow White's mother pricks her finger while embroidering on an ebony frame at a snowy window. As the drops of blood fall on the snow, she wishes for a daughter with skin as white as snow, lips as red as blood, and hair as black as ebony. The mother of the little boy in "The Juniper Tree" stands under a dark tree in white snow, peeling a red apple. She, too, cuts her finger and bleeds on the snow; she, too, wishes for a child as white as snow and red as blood.

In these two tales, the colors associated with the Great Goddess are being used to suggest the eternal feminine life cycle. Lederer refers to Io, the cow, who changed her color from white to rose to black, and associates her with the new moon (the White Goddess of birth and growth), the full moon (the Red Goddess of love and battle), and the old moon (the Black Goddess of death and divination): virgin, nymph, crone, the three aspects of the Great Goddess. Most heroines of tales are presented to us first in their white, or virgin, state. After they fulfill conditions of seclusion and trial and ride off with the prince, they are associated with the color red, or nubility; and all have a brush with transformation or death, which brings them in touch with the black.

Snow White herself is first innocent, or white; she meets her apparent death from eating the red side of the poisoned apple, analogous to menarche (or sexual knowledge, like Eve's); she goes into the "seclusion" of death, although the dwarfs will not bury her in the "black" ground; and she is revived by a kiss on her red lips, signifying marriage and nubility.

The colors appear in "The Twelve Brothers" in a more displaced fashion. In this story, red first means death. The birth of a daughter is announced to the doomed brothers by a flag: "It was not white, but blood red, to warn them that they were to die." The daughter plucks white lilies when she is old enough to be married; her action turns the brothers into black ravens, signifying the death of their human form or perhaps the impotence brought about by the presence of a nubile (menstruating) woman. The brothers are also represented by the lilies, and had a boy been born, they would have seen a white flag. This gives us an interesting situation in which the males are emblemized by white and black but not by red, menstrual blood; only the sister has any association with red in this tale.

Red is the most prevalent color in the stories and frequently appears as a rose. The rose or any flower is a dominant menstrual image in literature and folklore. A flower is also an image for the hymen. Because old beliefs associated the menarche with the breaking of the hymen, these correspondences persist. Thus, the briar roses that grow around Sleeping Beauty's castle and cause the death of the would-be penetrators may be allusions to the fear of defloration prevalent among primitive peoples and their association of defloration with the dangerous properties of menstrual blood. Another instance of symbolic defloration occurs in "Jorinda and Joringel": a witch changes a maiden into a nightingale, only to have her released from the charm when the lover wields a "blood-red" flower.

Red blood is itself an ever-present element in most fairy tales, which are full of the casual violence of childhood itself. Beheadings are as common as finger prickings and serve the same purpose: to provide the blood that keeps the plot moving. Blood from the severed head of the ugly daughter in "Sweetheart Roland" speaks to the wicked stepmother; the blood from Snow White's mother's finger becomes a symbol of Snow White's birth. In "The Goose Girl," three drops of her mother's blood on a handkerchief go with the heroine on her wedding journey, symbolizing the passing of the menstrual magic from mother to daughter; the blood speaks to the girl, giving her comfort and protecting her from the machinations of an evil servant who travels with her. When the heroine loses the handerkerchief with the blood, she loses her power, and the waiting woman almost wins the bridegroom.

But the most beautiful and meaningful use of blood in these tales to symbolize the life-giving menstrual fluid occurs in "The Juniper Tree." The true mother cuts her finger peeling a red apple while she is standing in the snow under the juniper tree. The drops of blood inspire her to wish, like Snow White's mother, for a child as red as blood and as white as snow:

> And as she said it, it made her feel very happy, as if it was really going to happen. And so she went into her house, and a month went by, the snow was gone; and two months, and every thing was green; and three months, and the flowers came up out of the ground; and four months, and all the trees in the woods sprouted and the tree branches grew dense and tangled with one another and the little birds sang so that the woods echoed, and the blossoms fell from the trees; and so five months were gone and she stood under the juniper tree and it smelled so sweet her heart leaped and she fell on her knees and was beside herself with happiness; and when six months had gone by, the fruit grew round and heavy and she was very still; and seven months and

she snatched the juniper berries and ate them so greedily she became sad and ill; and so the eighth month went by and she called her husband and cried and said, "When I die, bury me under the juniper." And she was comforted and felt happy, but when the nine months were gone, she had a child as white as snow and as red as blood and when she saw it she was so happy that she died.

This beautiful allegory of pregnancy and birth, encompassing the growth of life as well as the death that always lurks within the womb, is begun by woman's blood. The menstruation is the drops from the finger, which fertilize the ground under the juniper tree and cause both the baby and the tree to grow to fullness, making an indisputable connection between the mystery of woman's bleeding and the mystery of life that remains throughout the story.

Later, when the second wife murders the child born of the union between the woman and the tree, his sister, "weeping tears of blood," buries his bones under the juniper tree. This leads to an intensification of the blood-fertility correspondence. The spirit of the mother now inhabits the tree and receives new vitality from the bones of the child:

But the juniper began to stir and the branches kept opening out and coming back together again, just like something that is really happy. And then there was a sort of mist coming out of the tree and right in this mist it burned like fire and out of the fire flew this lovely bird that sang, oh, so gloriously sweet and flew high into the air and when it was gone the juniper tree was just the way it had always been and the cloth with the bones was gone.

In the original Grimm version of "Cinderella" (before Walt Disney), Cinderella's fairy godmother is her dead mother, whose spirit also resides in a tree. The tree grows over the mother's grave from a twig planted by Cinderella and watered by her tears. Cinderella prays to her mother for release from the cruelty of her stepsisters and for a gown for the prince's ball: "Shiver and shake, dear little tree / Gold and silver shower on me." The mother, in the form of a bird, grants Cinderella's wishes.

This repeated correspondence between the woman and

the tree—a source of life and strength, haven, refuge, and comfort—is consistent with the images of menstruation as flowers and of woman as flowering branch. It reflects one of the few positive attitudes toward menstruation in these stories from the childhood of our race.

Chapter 17

. . . .

ABSENT LITERATURE: THE MENARCHE

Uniquely female experiences are missing from most of literature. We learn of a male's attaining manhood in sexual initiation; much less frequently, of a woman's feelings on losing her virginity. We commonly see men rejoicing in the birth of a son, accepting that of a daughter, but Anaïs Nin is one of the few writers to portray the physical agonies of childbirth. Discussions of menstruation are rare, and generally present the male's point of view.

Even more rare is literary depiction of the menarche. This peculiarly female experience barely appears at all until the twentieth century in Western literature. Like her counterparts in other cultures, the Western girl who becomes a woman is generally hidden from view.

She is shown more often in diaries, in which she confides her fear, pride, ambivalence; later fiction writers use the menarche as a focus for the girl's developing attitudes toward men, herself, and other women. Finally, in recent fiction (undoubtedly influenced by feminism), the menarche becomes an occasion for celebration, an initiation into female culture.

The earliest fictional treatments of the menarche that we

have found are in French literature, in Edmond de Goncourt's "documentary novel" *Cherie* (1884) and Emile Zola's novel *La Joie de Vivre* [1] (1884). Goncourt conceived his *Cherie* while listening to the confidences of a princess's lady-in-waiting. Fascinated by the literary possibilities of female culture, he decided to write what would be his last novel about the life of a *jeune fille* growing up in fashionable Second Empire circles. Seeking the collaboration of women, Goncourt asked young girls to send him diaries, letters, confidences about growing up. He received many letters, some containing bizarre episodes or physiological details that would have appeared only in medical books in the 1880s.

The story he wove from the young girls' materials describes the life, coming-of-age, and death of Cherie Haudancourt, the daughter of a military officer and a Spanish mother who becomes insane. Not long after Cherie's first communion, she undergoes a transformation. Losing her childish grace, she becomes clumsy, awkward, almost comic; she trips over herself, does not know what to do with her hands and feet. She alternates between laughter and tears. Inwardly, she is changing from a little girl to *"une créature d'amour."* Goncourt interjects that although the medical profession insists that Parisian girls attain puberty at thirteen or fourteen, his letters from little girls mention numerous earlier cases, from nine to eleven; hence, his Cherie will menstruate early.

One day, Cherie awakens from a troubled sleep and finds unexpected and inexplicable blood. Five lines of dots follow, then Cherie's terrified thoughts: that she will have no more blood, that she will die because she cannot stop the blood from leaving her. She bursts into tears and is afraid to tell anyone what has happened to her.

The chambermaid enters, laughs mysteriously, and tries to remove the traces of Cherie's new state. For several months afterward, Cherie feels a little ashamed of her loss of blood, sensing it as a weakness and a strain, in her eyes having the disgraceful aspects that the Bible attributes to women in "that state." Cherie also becomes more timid and anxious around men.

Zola's *La Joie de Vivre* contains similar material about the menarche of Pauline Quenu, the cousin of the novel's hero.

Zola's Pauline, once studious, becomes inattentive, temperamental, nervous. Like Chérie, she is motherless. Zola is more precise about her physical changes; she gains swelling curves that feel congested and painful and "a light down like a black shadow in the most secret and delicate parts of her skin." Her aunt, with whom she lives, shrinks from telling Pauline what is soon to occur.

One morning, Pauline, like Chérie, wakes up on bloodied sheets. Pauline, "white with terror," is "screaming continuously for her aunt: her bare, parted legs were stained with blood, and she was staring at what had come out of her, all her habitual courage driven away by the shock." Her aunt tries to find "some lie which would calm her without telling her anything" and explains that it's like nosebleeding, and happens to all women. Pauline, unbelieving, faints and is insensible for several days.

Later, Pauline (like Zola, her creator) learns the truth from research in books. Surreptitiously reading her cousin's medical books, she learns at fourteen "things that are hidden from virgins until their wedding night." She gains a lifelong pity for suffering people, as well as understanding why "that red stream, the sign of her puberty, had poured from her as from a ripe grape crushed at the vine-harvest . . . that full tide of life that she felt surging within her." Ultimately, she becomes proud of "the rising tide of blood that broke in red rain."

Zola's imagery, richer than Goncourt's spare *histoire*, resembles that of later writers about menstruation, especially Anne Sexton and Sylvia Plath. Zola and Goncourt together introduce motifs that continue in later literature about the menarche: the girl's ignorance and fear, the timidity or refusal of other women to tell her what is happening to her, and the stained sheets, the palpable sign that she has entered the realm of womanhood.

As realists, Goncourt and Zola sought a slice of life, and the truth of their portrayals is reflected in diaries and autobiographies. But few, if any, fictional works treat the menarche between the 1880s and the 1920s.

Emma Goldman, the noted feminist and anarchist, published her autobiography, *Living My Life*, in 1931, but her menarche came in 1880 in Russia, when she was eleven. Like

Chérie and Pauline, she awoke one day "in great agony." She called her mother, who drew back the bedcovers and gave her the traditional slap Jewish mothers are expected to give their daughters.

> Suddenly I felt a stinging pain in my face. She had struck me. I let out a shriek, fastening on Mother's terrified eyes. "This is necessary for a girl," she said, "when she becomes a woman, as a protection against disgrace." She tried to take me in her arms, but I pushed her back. I was writhing in pain and I was too outraged for her to touch me. "I am going to die," I howled, "I want the *Feldscher*" [assistant doctor]. The *Feldscher* was sent for. He was a young man, a newcomer in our village. He examined me and gave me something to put me to sleep. Thenceforth, my dreams were of the *Feldscher*.

Emma Goldman's menarche, like Chérie's, led to her new awareness of men. Other diaries and novels, such as *A Young Girl's Diary,* include the central figure's changing consciousness about both men and women.

Freud was instrumental in the 1915 publication of *A Young Girl's Diary,* for which he wrote a prefatory letter. In the diary, a girl named Rita describes her life from ages eleven to fourteen and a half. Hers is an early description of what might be called *menarcheal competition:* girls' desire to be the first in their peer group to get their periods. But this competitive spirit is usually tinged with some embarrassment and ambivalence, as in Rita's report of her friend Hella's menarche.

Hella, bashful, does not want Rita to look at her. Hella's mother says, "Now you are not a child anymore, now you belong among the grown-ups." Hella is "a little puffed up about it"; like most of the schoolgirls, she feels herself entitled to "put on airs" now that it's happened. She swears her mother to secrecy so that her mother won't tell her father.

Not long afterward, in physics class, Rita's first period comes. She writes, "My goodness, to-day I have . . . , no, I can't write it plain out." Finally, she tells Hella, who kisses her on the street. But Rita dreads telling her aunt, with whom she lives, because she needs a "San- T-" (sanitary napkin or towel). She doesn't think she'll ever be able to buy one for herself, "even if I live to be 80. And it would be awful for Father to know about it."

Colette Audry, in her autobiography *Aux Yeux de Souvenir* (1947), is more than embarrassed about men's possible reactions. She feels "soiled" at her menarche, envies her younger sister's freedom. "Then I began to hate men, who would never experience that, who knew about it. And I detested women, who took it so easily, and who, if they knew about me, would gleefully think, 'Now it is your turn.' "

Nearly all writers about the menarche have some sense that it is to be hidden from males and, as in Rita's case, from grown-ups. Ignorance at the first period seems to have been a fact of life for many girls until recent years, and reticence about discussion could lead to terror for the girls.

Or reticence could lead to comic misapprehension, as Mary McCarthy reports in her autobiography, *Memories of a Catholic Girlhood*. When she was twelve and living in a convent boarding school, she cut her leg in athletics and bled on her bedsheet during the night. The next day, she asked the nun for a clean sheet. Mother Slattery announced that young Mary would be excused from athletics, then produced a "sort of cloth girdle and a peculiar flannel object which I first took to be a bandage." The bandage was, of course, a sanitary napkin. Although Mary protested that the blood was from a cut, neither Mother Slattery nor the mother superior (who explained "becoming a woman" later in the day) believed her. In order to keep peace, each month Mary

> reopened the cut on my leg, so as to draw a little blood to stain the napkins, which were issued me regularly, not only on this occasion, but every twenty-eight days thereafter. Eventually, I abandoned this bloodletting, for fear of lockjaw, and trusted to fate. Yet I was in awful dread of detection; my only hope, as I saw it, was either to be released from the convent or to become a woman in reality, which might take a year, at least.

Hence, even false menarche can be an occasion for anxiety.

A few diaries record girls' pride in becoming women. Anne Frank writes that "I have the feeling that in spite of all the pain, unpleasantness, and nastiness, I have a sweet secret." Thyde Monnier in *Moi* (1949) describes the pleasures of menarcheal competition: "Several of us had become 'big girls' during vacation; others reached that estate while at school, and then one after another we went 'to see the blood' in the courtyard water closets where they sat enthroned like queens receiving their subjects."

Menarcheal competition, like fear, pride, and ambivalence, is mentioned in fiction as well as nonfiction. So is generational tension and conflict between mother and daughter. In an early twentieth-century treatment of the menarche, Radclyffe Hall's controversial *The Well of Loneliness,* the heroine, Stephen Gordon, is very shy about discussing menstruation with other girls. Her attitude is a sign of her uneasiness with the female role, for she gradually learns she is a lesbian. Like many girls, Stephen wonders about her mother's female functions. "Had her mother shrunk back resentful, protesting when the seal of womanhood had been stamped upon her?" Stephen decides, with suggestions of both regret and envy, that her mother did not. For Stephen, however, the "seal of womanhood" may be a curse.

Within fifteen years after *The Well of Loneliness,* two other well-known novels handled the menarche in greater detail. One, by a man, treated the protagonist's resulting attitudes toward men, toward her body, and toward her memories. The second, by a woman, portrayed the heroine's subsequent attitudes toward other women.

The first girl, Christopher Morley's Kitty Foyle (1939), has her menarche on a train. She feels upset, but

> of course it proved to be the Curse, for the first time. I thought I was dying of tuberculosis, which in a vague way I knew caused hemorrhages. It must be a serious case because the hemorrhage had gone the wrong way.

She tells the porter, "I guess I'm sick," and "with the intuition of a great gentleman he must have guessed, for soon after a large black hand came through the curtains and handed me a package." She decides, as she later tells her lover Wyn, that Pullman porters are the finest gentlemen she knows.

There is a curious outsiderness to the tone, as if events occur only to be told, later, to Wyn. Even Kitty's abortion, later in the novel, is treated in the same way as her menarche, an outside event that happens to her but does not greatly touch her except in very small glimpses, as in her response to later porters making beds on the train with the green curtains: "just the look of them always gives me the preliminary cramps."

Francie's first period, in Betty Smith's *A Tree Grows in Brooklyn* (1943), is described with a greater degree of inwardness and in a cultural context involving women. Kitty Foyle, contemporaries might say, is male-identified; Francie is not. Francie has looked forward to being a woman; when she turns thirteen, she writes in her diary, "Today I am a woman." Then seeing her chest "as flat as a washboard," she rips the page out of her book. Francie is becoming a writer as well as an introspective woman, but she is as yet unformed in either role.

On the day of her menarche, Francie sees a group of women throwing stones at Joanna, a neighbor girl who gave birth to a child out of wedlock after her boyfriend's family (especially his mother and sisters) persuaded him not to marry her. Very upset at the stone throwing by those who are not without sin, Francie goes to the cellar of her house and feels "waves of hurt." She aches all over. When she tells her mother, Katie, the mother sighs and says, "So soon?" Katie tells her, "It's a natural thing that comes to all women. Remember always be a good girl because you can have a baby now. . . . You mustn't let the boys kiss you. . . . Remember Joanna." Francie thinks Katie has read her mind about Joanna and is amazed at her mother's insight.

Francie remembers Joanna and remembers how the other women treated her. Francie respects her mother and her aunts, who are the strong and sincere persons in her world, but resolves not to trust any woman because of women's disloyalty and cruelty to each other. The pain of giving birth "should make a bond that held them all together," thinks Francie, "it should make them love and protect each other against the man-world. But it was not so." Francie's menarche, then, is a point of departure for her reflections on what it means to be a woman. She has a vision of a female culture that is sisterly, not competitive or cruel, with the virtues of love and compassion traditionally associated with women.

For other female protagonists, too, the menarche is associated with reflections on what is and what ought to be. In

Rumer Godden's *Greengage Summer* (1958), the protagonist is thirteen-year-old Cecil, one of five English children unexpectedly spending the summer in a French hotel because of their mother's illness. Eliot, a man friendly to her and the other children, nevertheless turns out to be a jewel thief and murderer, and Cecil becomes confused about appearance and reality. Cecil's confusion about the world of adults is mirrored in her confusion about herself, when the "full tide" of her period appears. Eliot is the one who comforts her, telling her "now you are ready for love." Cecil is ecstatic at this unexpected male approval and thinks of Juliet, Cleopatra, Eve—and of her own plainness. But she later shows herself to be "manly," that is, brave and intrepid. The title of the book, like Zola's imagery in *La Joie de Vivre,* may refer not only to Cecil's physical ripeness but also to her sinking her teeth into unknown and previously forbidden knowledge.

When their first menstruation comes, most girls cry (if they can) for their mothers. One of the few treatments of the menarche from the mother's point of view is Jay Kennedy's *Prince Bart.* Valerie is the daughter of Bart, an actor, and his wife, Mollie, who are on the verge of divorce. Mollie tells Valerie, "This is an important event for you." Valerie nods and answers, "It's an awfully stickly feeling." Mollie shares her daughter's pride in being the first among her friends and tries to get Valerie not to refer to her condition as "the curse." Mollie wants Valerie to be proud, and yet Mollie feels her own life is in ruins. What can she say to make Valerie happy about being a woman? The sequence is a remarkable treatment of a mother's conflicting feelings about her daughter. Finally, Mollie pours wine for herself and Valerie, and they toast the girl's becoming a woman and then toast themselves.

In novels of the 1960s and early 1970s, the first menstruation frequently reveals cultural as well as generational tensions. Mother-daughter relationships are often the focus. In Ella Leffland's *Mrs. Munck* (1970), the menarche provides proof positive for the lack of closeness between mother and daughter:

> When the change did occur—and by that time I had grown used to the idea, had bowed, almost gracefully to the inevitable—I

was careful to keep it a secret from my mother. But that was not difficult, for by that time she had given up all hope of the smallest intimacy.

Similarly, in Joyce Carol Oates's *them* (1969), Maureen and her mother are unable to communicate about the "cramps." Maureen's menarche occurred at school with "a hot flow of blood, a terrible sickening surprise." Maureen's terror at her menarche is part of her general fastidiousness, her aversion to dirt and blood and sex.

In *Shadi* (1971), a juvenile novel by Margaret Embry, Emma's menarche becomes a symbol for the gap between the older and younger generations and cultures. Emma, a Navaho girl, is reluctant to participate in the *kinaaldá,* the traditional welcoming ceremony for girls who have their first period. Emma's grandmother, however, refuses to let her go to the Apache girls' dance, in which all the "girls who come to womanhood" are celebrated together. The grandmother insists on the separate, traditional *kinaaldá.* The grandmother tells Emma the old legends about Changing Woman, who was found by First Man and later fell in love with the sun. Emma listens, so she'll remember how to tell the story to her granddaughters, "though she wasn't sure they would think it very important."

Emma's celebration, which takes four days, concludes with a conflict between her family and local missionaries. *Shadi* records the folkways of another American culture in conflict with more modern standards. Emma's friend Ruby and other girls mock her for having the "old-fashioned" and "square" ceremony, and Emma feels torn between the old and the new. Her menarche is a rite of passage revealing a cultural split.

Cultural conflict over the menarche also appears in Toni Morrison's *The Bluest Eye* (1970). Pecola's initiation into womanhood has meaningful consequences in fixing her hatred for whites. Her sisters, Frieda and Claudia, attend Pecola, bringing her water and a napkin. Rosemary, a white girl, spies on the black children and tells Mama that the girls are "playing nasty." Mama begins to beat Pecola until she realizes that the child is "minstratin'." Later that evening, Claudia and

Frieda view Pecola with new respect. "Lying next to a real person who was really minstratin' was somehow sacred. She was different from us now—grown-up-like."

Some very recent fiction about the menarche treats it with comic deference, if not joy; possibly the influence of modern feminism has muted or eliminated ambivalence. The young narrator in Penelope Street's short story "The Magic Apple" sees a whole world of new possibilities surrounding her menarche. "My first day in Ann Arbor my first menstrual period began with a flourish. Some people call it a curse, but I called it a blessing. I was still a virgin, but I swore that wouldn't last for long. My breasts were starting to grow!"

Menarcheal competition in recent fiction becomes fierce, fast, and funny. Getting an early period is a mark of unambivalent distinction. Myrna in Peter Marks's *Hangups* tells her friend Sidney: "That was a very big summer. They gave me my first camera, and I got my first period. They all thought I was a genius for getting it so early. . . . You may think it's funny, but it's a very important moment in a woman's life."

The heroine in Julia Whedon's *Girl of the Golden West* is quite competitive: "It was at this time that I learned that Gay had just had her first period. I was devastated. Where was mine? What if I had to wait until I was fifteen or something? The Onset of the Menses. It had a noble ring."

In Sandra Hochman's *Walking Papers*, Eleanore Fishback is the first in the crowd to "fall off the roof." The others are jealous, and Eleanore, like Hella in *A Young Girl's Diary*, lords it over them.

> Eleanore came down the steps of Girls' Quarters swinging a sanitary napkin around her head as if it were a lasso and all the time yelling, "I've got it! I've got it" and we all huddled around her locker and made her tell us, in detail, what it was like. Yes, we were all grand inquisitors of the menstrual mystery.

Also new among recent women writers is an interest in the technology of handling menstruation. In *The Bluest Eye*, Pecola is taught how to use a sanitary napkin. In Lois Gould's *Such Good Friends,* there is a comic-horror episode in which the protagonist learns to insert a tampon, aided by two friends in the school lavatory. The instruction folder is horrifying: "The diagrams—terrifying cross-sections of the female interior, full of squiggly Suez canals—showed a cute little cotton wad nestled in there like an eensy white mouse with its tail hanging down and out."

Already scared, Julie can't find the spot. Then she's afraid it won't work because she's a virgin; the instructions say "unmarried girls" and nothing about "hymen." The girls are very anxious that no one should come in during Julie's lesson, although what they are doing is a bathroom function. When Julie is afraid she'll fail, her friend Peggy says, "Just don't tell me how you hate sanitary belts and how *icky* it all is." Whatever mystique there is surrounds the act of using a tampon, not the menstruation. After all the graphic groping, Julie finally succeeds and writes in her memory book: "Today I became a woman."

Sasha Davis's initiation into womanhood in Alix Kates Shulman's *Memoirs of an Ex-Prom Queen* is also a comic adventure suitable to an explicit and technological age. When her first period comes, Sasha emits the primal scream for her mother. "I knew for sure I was a freak," she confides to the reader. She's afraid her solitary hobby will be discovered: "I was sure my curious finger had injured something." She gets blood on the bath mat, in the bath water, on her fingers, on her towel—"everything I touched was getting soiled."

Her mother proceeds to give her a lesson in the use of sanitary napkins, like "a stewardess demonstrating the oxygen mask." Sasha is sure no one else has this awful bleeding, and everyone will know she bleeds "down there." After her menarche, Sasha reports, "I tried to pass as normal, but inside I knew I was a freak."

Shulman and Gould, although humorous in their treatments of menstrual nitty-gritty, seem to regard periods as laughable out of a slight desperation: Periodic bleeding is an inevitable occupational hazard of being a young woman. There is one book, however, that presents an entirely positive view of the menarche and may point a new direction. The book is a juvenile novel we mentioned earlier in the book, Judy Blume's *Are You There God? It's Me, Margaret.*

Margaret Simon is a girl waiting, with her three close friends who form the "Pre-Teen Sensations Club," for their periods to come. They enjoy visiting the sanitary napkin displays in the drugstore but run when the male clerk looks at them. There is a friendly but not frantic menarcheal competition, and Margaret tries to get an edge on her opponents by praying to God. She offers a deal: She'll be good around the house if He'll give her some breasts.

A week later, "Gretchen got it." The others, shrieking, want to know all about it: What did her mother say? How could she stand to keep a washcloth in her pants while her mother was going to the drugstore to get pads? How did it feel? Did it make her feel older? Gretchen is very calm.

When her friend Nancy is next, Margaret sees Nancy, who has lied and said she's had a period before, become scared and hysterical. Gretchen and Nancy appear as positive and negative role models. As other women usually do in fiction, they serve to define the possibilities and limits of action for the central female character. Margaret can be calm or frantic.

Finally, when Margaret is packing for camp, "it" comes. She sees blood on her underwear, "not a lot—but enough." She starts to laugh and cry at the same time, and so does her mother, who brings her some "Teenage Softies." Her mother offers to show her how to use the napkin, but Margaret stops her. "Mom, I've been practicing in my room for two months!" Both of them laugh. Reverently, Margaret locks the bathroom door, attaches a Teenage Softie to the little hooks on her pink belt, gets dressed, and looks in the mirror. Then she thanks God that it came.

Although *Are You There God?* is an odd book (girl-gets-napkin), it is an exceptionally warm one in the attitudes expressed toward women. The mothers are understanding and good-humored. Margaret's grandmother, who carries a shopping bag filled with corned beef and pickles from New York because she's sure such delicacies cannot be had in New Jersey, is a lovable eccentric. Margaret has the kind of friends and family Francie, in *A Tree Grows in Brooklyn*, would have liked.

Furthermore, *Are You There God?* presents some clues to why the menarche is usually absent from literature. Not only are women writers underrepresented in literature, but males have had, since Adam named Eve, the power of defining reality, that is, of saying what is important and what is not. Confrontation with a white whale, though unlikely, is at least a possible experience for males and therefore of possible significance. Having a first period is neither possible for men nor does it affect them. Hence, it can be dismissed—and usually is.

Are You There God? insists on the centrality of the female experience. The protagonist and the significant characters are all female, and they define what is and what is not important in their universe. Female culture consists of those experiences that are not accessible to men and that until recently have been undervalued by both women and men.

A survey of menarcheal literature reveals the shifting emphasis and the interplay between art and life. When female experience is more valued in life, it takes on more positive roles in art. The menarche, once an event surrounded with fear, terror, and ignorance, can today be seen as a treasured moment, the moment of becoming a woman.

. . . .

Chapter 18

THE MIRACLE OF BLOOD: MENSTRUAL IMAGERY IN MYTH AND POETRY

Direct references to menstrual blood are uncommon in myth and poetry. Usually, the unmentionable is not mentioned. Or else, the menstrual flow, when it does appear, invariably appears in disguise, as an image or symbol, ranging from the full moon to the garbage dump. Literary critics have been either unconscious of or uninterested in the possible menstrual significance of certain myths and poems. Claude Dagmar Daly and Clark Griffith are two exceptions.

In 1935, Daly published a psychoanalytic essay entitled "The Menstruation Complex in Literature." He argued that the menstruation complex, the revulsion toward and denial of the menstruating woman, was at the root of the Oedipus complex. The menstruating woman is a continual reminder of the male's fear of castration and death, a figure so threatening that she is buried deep in the unconscious mind. She emerges nonetheless in myth and dreams.

Daly's theory of the menstruation complex has received scant attention both from psychoanalysts and from literary critics, presumably, he would have argued, because the idea is too unpleasant to face. Yet, menstrual imagery is "everywhere," claimed Daly, who concentrated his own analysis on the poetry of Charles Baudelaire and the poetry and stories of Edgar Allan Poe. Daly thought that Poe's story "The Masque of the Red Death" fully captured the menstruation trauma. The red, disease-bearing visitor comes like a "pall of death, shutting out the pre-historic past." [1]

In 1964, another male critic, Clark Griffith, found menstrual themes in the poetry of Emily Dickinson. Griffith buried this insight in the epilogue of his study of Dickinson, *The Long Shadow*. Although Griffith viewed menstrual cramps as Dickinson's major problem, he kept his secret until the end of the book, and he kept "menstruation" out of the index.

Griffith contended that the "rhythm of suffering" so prevalent in Dickinson's poetry was the menstrual rhythm. Because she wanted to be a man, because she desired a penis, Dickinson saw menstruation as "an affront and a burden." Her main poetic voice, said Griffith, is "the helpless, abused, harassed, tormented female," who expresses her menstrual problems through a trio of images: the clock (a symbol of the repetition of pain), the father (the envied male who doesn't menstruate), and childhood (the only state in which pain could be escaped). The menstrual theme, of which Dickinson was utterly unconscious, was greatest in her thirties and forties, "when her spinsterish prejudices and their consequences were probably most demanding." By universalizing her pain, by moving from the personal to the tragic, Dickinson turned her "sickness" into great art, "while another woman, confronted with the same grave issues, might have become an hysteric, a feminist, a lesbian, a religious tractarian, or an agressive shrew." [2]

Clark Griffith is not alone in explaining Dickinson's achievement as a poet in terms of her penis envy, her Oedipus complex, her failure at femininity. His mention of the unmentionable, however, sets him apart. Unfortunately, Griffith's understanding of the psychology of menstruation is based on the works of Helene Deutsch and Mary Chadwick rather than on the more reasonable conclusions of Karen Horney and Clara Thompson. His evaluation of Dickinson displays a negative attitude toward menstruation and female sexuality. Daly's examples of menstrual imagery (redness, fluid, and the moon) seem more to the point than Griffith's psychology.

A number of poetic symbols may at times signify menstruation: sickness, mud, volcanoes, the arrival of a visitor, bathing, dumping garbage, falling from a high place, odors, leakages, stains, clocks, swamps, rags, tamps, tidal rhythms, and the colors red, pink, and purple. But the most universal images are flowers, fluid, witches, and the moon. Like other images, the ones suggesting menstruation do so only at times and only within a particular context. Red can sometimes represent the menstrual flow, but it is also open to a variety of other interpretations, such as anger, jealousy, war, adultery, and suffering. Or it may have no symbolic meaning at all. Dickinson uses the word *red* in thirty poems, usually to describe the setting sun. In only four of her poems does red seem to signify menstruation. Nonetheless, an openness toward menstruation as a symbolic possibility in poetry can lead to a fresh reading of some familiar works.

FLUID

Of all menstrual symbols, the one most clearly connected to the monthly flux is blood. At times, however, the mythmaker or dreamer or poet disguises the blood, converting it into a sacred river, a tide, a flood, or some other liquid. This process of conversion is vividly conveyed in a speech by the nineteenth-century feminist Victoria Woodhull, who saw menstruation as a river of waste. In Woodhull's vision of the New Jerusalem, menstruation would cease, and the "perverted" flow would become "a pure river of the water of life proceeding out of the throne of the God." [3]

Some of the early Flood myths may have been in part a response to the dread of the menstruating woman. Although there is no evidence of this meaning in the Flood myths of the Hebrews or the Greeks, it seems fairly obvious in the Babylonian myth of the creation of the earth.

In that myth, Tiamat, the Mother of All and the symbol of chaos, creates monsters whose blood is poison and unleashes them on the world. She is defeated by her son, Marduk, who "cut channels for the blood to flow out of her, and he bade the winds bear her blood away into the secret places." He then splits her body in two, sending half of it into the sky and bolting it in place to prevent floods and from the other half making the earth. Marduk is the ordering principle, who must destroy chaos before he can govern. The emphasis in this myth on chaos, flooding, and blood suggests that before he himself can come into power, the male must subdue and divide the body of woman, whose danger lies in her unpredictable fluid.

Emily Dickinson occasionally uses fluid images in a way that suggests menstruation:

> The name—of it—is "Autumn"—
> The hue—of it—is Blood—
> An artery—upon the Hill—
> A Vein—along the Road—
>
> Great Globules—in the Alleys—
> And Oh, the Shower of Stain—
> When Winds—upset the Basin—
> And spill the Scarlet Rain—
>
> It sprinkles Bonnets—far below—
> It gathers ruddy Pools—
> Then—eddies like a Rose—away—
> Upon Vermillion Wheels—

Red is the dominant hue of this poem about autumn, the time of death and of witches.

In Edna St. Vincent Millay's poem about menstruation, called "Menses," the fluid comparisons are to "ugly" snake venom and "innocent" oil; menstrual blood is "poison." The venom motif is carried throughout the poem with references to "coiling," "fangs drawn," and "strike again." The final two lines recall the Satan-snake plunging into the abyss, or menstrual hell. Millay's "Menses" is one of the few poems in English directly about menstruation. As the subtitle indicates, the images derive from a male point of view: *"(He speaks, but to himself, being aware how it is with her)."* The snake and poison images reveal unequivocally the male fear of the menstrual process.

Another poem specifically about menstruation is Nadine Mac Donald's "On Menstruating in the Middle of a Lecture on the Fall of the Roman Empire," which we quote in its entirety:

Three weeks late, three weeks of wearing
clean Kotex as a guard, three weeks
of looking behind me as a [sic] I walked, three
weeks of renouncing sex; of not wearing
white pants. And yet it started, recapitulated
somewhere between Caesar and the coliseums,
a spot minute, like a leak in a dike.
It spread like a chest wound under a toga.
During the rhetoric there were stirrings
in me, like history. It betrays me
like Brutus; my monthly let; late,
released upon my yellow taffeta:
My mark remains, slowly conquering
the white velvet of the wing chair,
leaving the cradle of civilization in its wake.

The menstrual imagery here is unconventional. Rather than a tide or a flood, the menstrual fluid is a "leak in a dike." The dominant image is of battle; the menses spreads "like a chest wound," conquers the wing chair. The word *let* means an obstacle, something that must be overcome; yet, the word also contains the idea of release of flow, as in "to let blood." In the context of Roman (and male) history, menstruation is the betrayer of Caesar.

Mac Donald has captured in this poem the ironic contradictions between traditional male and female roles. Woman wears taffeta, stains her white pants, looks behind herself as she walks; man fights battles, builds empires, records history, looks ahead. In "On Menstruating in the Middle of a Lecture on the Fall of the Roman Empire," Mac Donald assimilates both roles with great discomfort but emerges victorious, leaving her menstrual mark on Western culture.

FLOWERS

A rich and important symbol for the menstruating woman is the flower. Flowers symbolize fertility and delicacy. They are pretty and decorative rather than useful. They give off odors. They easily wilt and decay. In the Bible, the word *flowers* means menstrual blood: "if any man lie with her at all, and her flowers be upon him, he shall be unclean seven days" (Leviticus 15:24).

Flowers have similar meaning in the Greek myth of Persephone. This myth, first mentioned in Hesiod's *Theogony*, has been treated by Ovid, Spenser, Milton, and Shelley, among others. The versions vary, but in each, Persephone is seduced while gathering flowers.

In Ovid's version, Persephone (Proserpina) and the daughters of Ocean pick violets and white lilies. "And while with girlish eagerness she was filling her basket and her bosom and striving to surpass her mates in gathering, almost in one act did Hades [Pluto] see and love and carry her away; so precipitate was his love." In the abduction, Persephone's garment is torn. Her flowers fall from her tunic, "and such was the innocence of her girlish years, the loss of her flowers even at such a time aroused new grief." Hades chariots her through deep lakes and pools until he reaches a bay inhabited by the water nymph Cyane, who tries to stop him. But Hades opens Cyane's pool and plunges with his bride into the underworld. In her grief, Cyane melts, limb by limb, into the water. "And finally, in place of living blood, clear water flows through her weakened veins and nothing is left that you can touch." Cyane's changing from blood to water, from the threatening to the subdued, is similar to Tiamat's blood flowing underground into secret places and to Victoria Woodhull's dream of a New Jerusalem.

Bullfinch, who records the legend in his *Age of Fable*, comments that Persephone "signifies the seed-corn which when cast into the ground lies there concealed." Yet, in Bullfinch's version, flowers, not seeds, fall from Persephone's apron. The fallen flower is on one level an emblem for defloration, the breaking of the hymen. The flower may also be a symbol for Persephone's wasted menstrual blood.

In *Interpretation of Dreams*, Freud records a dream of flowers, which he interpreted as having menstrual significance. The patient dreamed that she was descending from a high place. "As she climbs she is carrying *a big branch* in her hand, really like a tree, which is thickly studded with *red flowers.*" [4] As she descends, the flowers, which look like red camellias, begin to fall. Freud reads both the blossoming branch and the falling flowers as symbols for menstruation. The patient, in analysis, had associated the bough with a lily and herself with the angel of the Annunciation. The dream, Freud argues, represents both sexual purity, symbolized by the lily, and sexual guilt, symbolized by the red camellia. The bough is an allusion to Dumas's *La Dame aux Camélias*, in which Camille wore a white flower except during her period, when she wore a red one. This interpretation seems applicable to the Persephone myth as well. Persephone is both pure and sexual, the virgin and the temptress. In most versions of the myth, the flowers she picks are white and purple, the lily and the violet. (Freud, who often went to Greek mythology to explain human behavior, makes no reference to the Persephone myth in this context.)

What finally attracts Hades to Persephone is her flowers. In the Homeric hymn, flowers are Persephone's temptation as well; she is raped after being drawn away from the group in pursuit of a "most marvelous flower, with a hundred blooms and a delicious fragrance." The fragrance is compelling. In his essay on "The Taboo of Virginity," Freud speculates that in the prehistoric past, menstrual blood was a sexual stimulus. Men were once, like animals, sexually drawn to the smell of menstruation. But when man assumed an upright gait, he repressed this attraction. In Ovid, it is clear that Hades "falls in love" at the same moment that he sees the flowers, as if Hades were sexually stimulated by the scent.

The flower is the key symbol in the poetry of Baudelaire. Daly, in his study of Baudelaire and Poe, quotes from several poems that show a repugnance for flowers and for women. In "The Martyr," for example, a bleeding, decapitated corpse lies, like a flower, in a warm, perfumed room. In his analysis, Daly views the perfume as the mother's menstrual odor, the corpse as the bleeding (menstruating and castrated) vagina.

Applying Daly's insights to *Les Fleurs du Mal*, we have noticed a snake or an odor or a ruined flower or a secretion on almost every page. In "The Blessing," for instance, *"boutons empestés"* (blighted buds) fall from a branch. In "Beacons,"

Baudelaire refers to Delacroix's *"lac du sang hantée des mauvais anges"* ("lake of blood haunted by evil angels"). The title of his best-known collection, *Les Fleurs du Mal*, is translated as *Flowers of Evil*. But the word *mal* also means "sickness," and the flowers appear to represent, on a secondary level, flowers of sickness, of menstruation.

Some women poets have likened the ripening of flowers to the ripening of their bodies. In a poem called "Moonrise," Sylvia Plath contrasts white, symbol here of purity and death, with red, symbol of life and ripeness. At the poem's conclusion, Plath equates the berry's redness with her own fluids, its fertility with hers: "The berries purple/And bleed. The white stomach may ripen yet." In a poem called "Gardener," Erica Jong describes the inside of her womb in colors of poppies and bougainvillea.

Anne Sexton also uses the bleeding flower image, for example, in "The Wedding Night," where a twelve-year-old flower girl is compared with more "sure-bodied" buds: "Not one of them had trickled blood." The reference is to the potential budding-bleeding of the flower girl and to the breaking of the bride's hymen. In another poem about her own childhood, Sexton recalls how, at the age of six, she "lived in a graveyard full of dolls," unaware of her flesh, of the "exotic flower" that would soon bloom inside her. Sexton's most specific reference to menstrual flowers is in her poem "Menstruation at Forty." As her birthday approaches, she longs for a son, but it is too late; it is the "November of the body," and the year and the harvest are finished. Sexton is approaching menopause; menstrual blood comes as a sign of the womb's failure to bear a male before the end of her fertile season. The two days of menstrual bleeding are deathdays, symbolized by flowers bleeding from her wrist. The flowers are also funeral wreaths, emblems of the death of her womb. The bleeding corsage, fallen rose petals, blighted buds, spotted geraniums—these menstrual images dominate in poetry concerned with woman's fertility and with her seasons of harvest and death. Rarely does one find a poet comparing menstruation with the cycle of the mighty oak or the spreading chestnut. The flower, both perishable and reproductive, has traditionally worn woman's color and shared her perfume.

In a poem written by May Sarton in 1937, woman is strong, her seed the seed of the tree of life.

There were seeds
within her
that burst at intervals
and for a little while
she would come back
to heaviness,
and then before a surging miracle
of blood,
relax,
and re-identify herself,
each time more closely
with the heart of life.
'I am the beginning,
the never-ending,
the perfect tree.'
And she would lean
again as once
on the great curve of the earth,
part of its turning,
as distinctly part
of the universe as a star—
as unresistant,
as completely rhythmical.

THE WITCH

If the tree in Sarton's "She Shall Be Called Woman" represents the strength and resilience of the menstruating woman, her "surging miracle of blood," so the witch traditionally represents her wickedness, her demonic excretions. The fearful ugliness of the traditional witch is an appropriate symbol of the woman whose life-giving blood has dried. The season of the witch is autumn, what Plath calls "the month of red leaves"; Dickinson, "the hue of blood"; Sexton, the "November of the body." In autumn, Demeter punishes the world for the rape of Persephone. Flowers decay and fall. Witches ride the sky to the dark light of the old moon.

The witch is a major symbol in Sexton's poetry. In "The Double Image," a poem that begins in November, she recalls her suicide attempt following the birth of her daughter. The "green witches" in her head remind us of the hags traditionally associated with destroying mothers' milk, causing madness, carrying away children. Here they are related to bodily flow, to leaking doom. The witch-fluid image combines the ideas of blood, milk, and the suicidal poison: "The white men pumped the poison out."

Plath also associates witches with autumn and sickness. The time for witch burning is October, "month of red leaves," of burning dry sticks in the marketplace; the "hag" in Plath's poem "Maudlin" is also a menstruating witch, eternally linked with the moon's "curse."

Muriel Rukeyser writes about witches in "Mrs. Walpurga." (The name comes from Saint Walpurga, an eighth-century British nun who became, in the Middle Ages, a protector against magic and incantations.) In her Walpurgis Night dream, the persona sees and psychologically embraces the spirits that had seemed dead in her: the lost years, the children, the couples copulating in the dark. At the climax of the poem, in a passage rich with images of fluid, flowers, and the moon, Mrs. Walpurga is reborn into the life-giving night.

The complex "Mrs. Walpurga" presents the persona of a withered witch against an affirmation of woman's moon-linked periodicity. In myth and poetry, much depends upon the association of menstruation with the moon.

THE MOON

The word *menstruation* means "moon change." German peasants have long referred to menstruation as "the moon"; in France, it is called *le moment de la lune*. In non-Western cultures, we find similar associations. In Saibai and Yam, two islands off the northern tip of Australia, people believed that menstruation was caused by the moon, who came in the form of a man to seduce the pubescent girl. Their word for moon, *ganumi*, is often used as a substitute for *nanumud*, or menstrual blood.[5]

Menstrual seclusion rituals are frequently determined by the phases of the moon. Women in one African clan are isolated for two moons: "For one moon and another moon you

have hidden yourself away from profane eyes, you have whit-
ened your bodies so that death will not carry them off to his
village," the people chant as the girls return from their menstrual huts.[6] The Juluo, from the district of Kavirondo in East
Africa, believed that menstruation came with the new moon
and that only then could women become pregnant.[7] Darwin,
observing that both moon and menstrual cycles were of
twenty-eight days' duration, actually theorized that menstruation was directly related to the action of the moon on the
tides and began when we were all sea creatures.

In some cultures, the moon is a bridegroom responsible
for causing the first menstruation. The bridegroom-moon of a
New Guinea legend pursued women without success until
one took pity on him. After she became pregnant, the jealous
husband threw the moon man into the fire. His blood flew to
the sky and became the moon. As punishment, from that time
on, all women were condemned to bleed at his apparition
except for the very young, the very old, and the pregnant.[8]
Among the Maori of New Zealand, menstruation is called
mata marama ("moon sickness").

For poets, the moon is an eternal symbol—of death, of the
mother, of the imagination, of virginity, of immortality. The
moon is also, for many, a menstrual image. William Butler
Yeats constructed a vision, a culture, and a poetic mythos
around the cycles of the moon. "Twenty-and-eight the phases
of the moon, / The full and the moon's dark and all the cres-
cents," Yeats writes in *A Vision*. The birth of the hero occurs
in phase twelve; the thirteenth phase "sets the soul at war."
Phase seventeen, shortly after the full moon, is the phase of
"Unity of Being," the phase of Shelley, Dante, and Yeats himself. Yeats turned his lunary visions into poetic symbol.

One source of Yeats's symbolism was his uncle George
Pollexfen, who shared his dreams and his residence with a
"second-sighted servant" named Mary Battle. Mary had
frequent dreams of blood, as did Yeats's uncle. One night, the
uncle had an infection, a "blood-poisoning" following vacci-
nation for smallpox. At the peak of his delirium, George saw
"dancing red figures." A little later, he told Yeats, "There is a
river running through the room." Yeats advised him to get rid
of the figures by invoking Gabriel, the "angel of the Moon,"

who could command the waters. When the red men reappeared, the uncle was able to send them away. This metacommunication between Yeats and George Pollexfen, recorded in *The Autobiography of William Butler Yeats,* is remarkably similar to what Daly, in discussing the poetry of Poe and Baudelaire, calls the "menstruation complex" images: redness, rivers running in and out of rooms, the tide-controlling moon.

In his poetry, Yeats uses many of these images, most fully in the 1933 volume *The Winding Stair and Other Poems,* which includes one of his greatest poems, "Byzantium," with its haunting refrain "mire or blood." Blood and mire are for Yeats symbols of the flesh and change, contrasted in the poem with the permanent, hard images of "bird and golden handiwork." The moon of "Byzantium" is associated with the cyclical blood and change of human life. In "Blood and Moon," the tower and the moon represent nonchange or art; whereas the blood symbolizes frenzy and impermanence. The word *blood* is used eight times in "Blood and Moon," most memorably in the line "Odour of blood on the ancestral chair!" In the poem "Oil and Blood," there is reference to the odor of violets and to "bodies of the vampires full of blood; / Their shrouds are bloody and their lips are wet." "Oil and Blood" is followed in *The Winding Stair* by a strange poem, "Veronica's Napkin," which ends with the line "A pattern on a napkin dipped in blood." (Veronica is the woman in the New Testament who wiped Christ's face with her veil.) The various napkin, blood, mire, oil, and stain images running through Yeats's poetry—literally hundreds—are bound together by the overwhelming presence of the moon, whose biological significance Yeats makes apparent in "The Crazed Moon": "Crazed through much child-bearing / The moon is staggering in the sky." Depending on her cycle, the moon is staggering or crazed or pure or arrogant, as are the rough beasts under her influence.

In his last volume of poetry, the poem "The Circus Animals' Desertion" traces the various themes and images of Yeats's poetry to their primal source, "the foul rag-and-bone shop of the heart." It seems possible that Yeats's images were born from the rags and refuse of the bleeding slut-mother, who is cyclically purified as she goes through her phases—from old to new to full moon, from Crazy Jane to the Holy Virgin to Helen, from crone to virgin to whore.

For Plath, as for Yeats, the moon is a major symbol, one that she uses quite often in conjunction with two other menstrual images, the tide and the witch. The menstruating moon appears in the poem "Lesbos." In "Childless Woman," she presents the idea we found in Sexton's "Menstruation at Forty": that menstrual flow means the failure of the empty womb. In "The Munich Mannequins," after describing the purposeless, monthly "unloosing" of moons, she writes, "The blood flood is the flood of love, the absolute sacrifice."

Gary Snyder, in "In Praise of Sick Women," uses most of the menstrual images discussed here: falling rain, blighted fruit, berries, bleeding tides. The poem concludes with a reference to the age-old ritual of menstrual seclusion: "in a bark shack." An untitled prose poem by Poe is another work by a man that seems rich in menstrual images, not only the red fluid but also flowers and the moon:

> It was night, and the rain fell; and falling it was not rain, but, having fallen, it was blood. And I stood in the morass among the tall lilies, and the rain fell upon my head—and the lilies sighed one unto the other in the solemnity of their desolation.
>
> And, all at once, the moon rose through the then ghastly mist, and was crimson in color.

In "Planetarium," a poem commemorating the astronomer Caroline Herschel, Adrienne Rich uses the moon-tide image to convey the timelessness of the female experience.

We can expect new incantations from women as well as from men as they struggle to find new means of poetic expression. As the old mythology encounters the new menstrual consciousness, a new vision of woman should inform the poetry of our age.

Chapter 19

. . . .

MENSTRUAL MADNESS IN DRAMA AND FICTION

Irrationality is the quality most commonly attributed to the menstruating woman in popular mythology. Most portrayals of menstruation are negative, evoking fear, disgust, loathing, or other hostile attitudes toward women. Only recently have writers given menstruation positive mythic overtones, as a heroic ritual shared by the community of women, connecting them both with the rhythms of nature and with each other.

The first overt mention of menstruation on stage may be in August Strindberg's *Miss Julie*. The title character forgets her station in life and dances wildly with her servants, her social inferiors. One servant explains to another, "Oh, it's just her time coming on. She's always queer then." [1] In more recent works, the myth remains: Helman in Alison Lurie's *Love and Friendship* asks why Emmy is carrying on: "Are you having your period?" In Clare Booth Luce's version of *A Doll's House*, Nora perceives a similar attitude in her husband: "He is saying to himself, she's not having her period, she's not pregnant, she's not jealous; it's *got* to be another man."

In John Fowles's *The French Lieutenant's Woman*, menstrual irrationality is associated with psychotic behavior. The naïve Charles learns much about women's "nature" by studying the case of Marie de Morrell, who had accused an innocent man of rape. A physician later discovered that the obscene letters used to convict the rapist "fell into the clear monthly—or menstrual—pattern." Marie had written these obscene (psychotic, hysterical, irrational, monthly) letters to herself.

The myth that links menstruation and irrationality is not solely an old-fashioned idea, nor is it an idea confined to the community of men. Anaïs Nin uses it in *A Spy in the House of Love,* as do Alice Munro in *Lives of Girls and Women* and Joyce Elbert in *The Crazy Ladies.* These writers apparently share a belief that women are at the mercy of their menstrual flow.

The myth that menstruation means madness touches on another myth: the idea that the menstruating woman is disgusting, if not taboo. For several of Faulkner's characters, menstruation provides the negative definition of a woman. Quentin Compson's father in *The Sound and the Fury* sees women as a "delicate equilibrium of periodical filth between two moons balanced." In *Light in August,* a boy tells others about women: "the smooth and superior shape in which volition dwelled doomed to be at stated and inescapable intervals victims of periodical filth." A little later in the same book, Joe Christmas runs away from a girl who refuses sex because of "the day of the month"; he vomits.

The use of menstruation as a negative condition is not confined to male writers. In Janet Frame's *Faces in the Water,* a woman expresses her madness by hoarding used sanitary napkins, an action that links irrationality and loathing as two aspects of menstruation in fiction. (Aubrey Beardsley reportedly asked his female friends to send him their used menstrual rags.)

The taboo on intercourse during menstruation, a conscious embodiment of a more primordial fear, is mentioned in countless works, including Alexandre Dumas's *La Dame aux Camélias,* Sue Kaufman's *Dairy of a Mad Housewife,* Gail Parent's *Sheila Levine is Dead and Living in New York,* Gisela Elsner's "The Initiation," Henry Miller's *Tropic of Cancer,* Joyce Carol Oates's *them.* Even O, the sexually experimental heroine in Pauline Réage's *The Story of O*, prefers to make excuses, not love, when her female lovers have their periods. All these examples are simply incidents in the books, not a part of the overall theme. In some books, however, the taboo on intercourse during menstruation pervades the entire work. Undoubtedly, the best example is the case of Yakov Bok in Bernard Malamud's *The Fixer*.

Yakov, a Jew, rejects making love to the crippled Zina when he sees blood running down her leg. He tells her that she is unclean; he remembers that even his wife, who left him, was modest about her periods. Because he rejects her, Zina later charges him with assault. Yakov's disgust becomes, ironically, a part of his own destruction.

The Fixer is pervaded with disgust and fear surrounding blood. Yakov is accused of being a drinker of blood; he is said to be an example of the bloodguilt of the Jewish nation in Christ's death; he even has hallucinations about the czar and blood, and his gentile captors expect him to menstruate. Menstruation defines a woman as inferior, on the same level as a Jew. The menstrual taboo in *The Fixer* may be seen as the pattern for all the taboos in the book because it unites the fear and loathing of blood with similar attitudes or community myths about women.

Perhaps in an effort to counteract the "dangers" of the menstruating woman, many writers find it necessary to demystify menstruation. By treating it in a more matter-of-fact way, they strip away some of the fear and loathing. In Cervantes's *Don Quixote*, for example, menstruation seems to be a sign of earthly order, a touchstone of everyday reality. Cervantes's Don has a seriocomic, probably hallucinated adventure in the enchanted underworld Cave of Monestinos. While he is there, he sees the Lady Belerma; his guide, Montesinos, explains that she is under a spell, which causes the great rings around her eyes and her sickly complexion: "Do not suppose," he added, "that her sallowness and the rings round her eyes spring from the monthly disorders common to women, for it is many months, or even years, since these have even appeared at her gates. They arise from the grief in her heart." Enchantment, then, does not preclude real life processes; her age, not her enchantment, prevents her from menstruating.

Menstruation also functions as an unmasking in Joan Didion's *Play It as It Lays*. Maria Wyeth's abortionist tries to calm any possible emotional difficulties by telling her that the abortion is just "induced menstruation." Maria does not believe him, and later, she finds part of the placenta on the pad she is wearing. The doctor's saying it's menstruation is intended to diminish Maria's fears, but it also shows her what she knew all along: that few people can be trusted.

In both works, menstruation is demystified; the writers suggest that grief and abortion are more worthy of human concern. Menstruation is also demystified when it is mentioned inappropriately, as in a test of morality: in Dan Wakefield's *Going All the Way*, the reader learns that "Nice girls didn't do it when they had the rag on." Not loathing; merely custom.

Graphic details about menstruation tend to have a similar effect: If you know how it's handled, how can it be taboo or enchanted? Many modern writers describe the use of menstrual paraphernalia: Doris Lessing in *The Golden Notebook*, Lois Gould in *Such Good Friends*, Alix Kates Shulman in *Memoirs of an Ex-Prom Queen* (Sasha Davis brags that "my Kotex disposal was down to an art"), Toni Morrison in *The Bluest Eye*. Such writers dispel male fantasies or myths surrounding female functionings, such as Erik Erikson's statement that each menstruation is "a crying to heaven in mourning over a child." [1]

Some characters take menstruation into their own hands, using it or its paraphernalia for their own ends. In Lois Gould's *Necessary Objects*, a woman prominently displays a Kotex box so that her catty friends will know that she's still "young enough," has not reached menopause. A character in *The Crazy Ladies* does not like to wear underpants, so wears Pursettes to keep warm. In Marge Piercy's *Small Changes*, Beth uses ketchup to fake a period to avoid intercourse with her traditionalist husband. In Mario Puzo's *The Fortunate Pilgrim*, a young but not inexperienced bride uses her menstruation to fake the necessary virginal bleeding. What unites these disparate examples is the woman's control of the situation, her refusal to yield to myth, her insistence on shaping convention for her own uses.

Most mentions of menstruation in fiction and drama are brief. We have not even mentioned the countless works that show a missed period as a sign of pregnancy. These take us outside the realm of myth, although today they may involve a portrayal of greater female autonomy. In *Small Changes,* for instance, a group of women create a comedy skit in which a woman tells her beau she missed her period. What used to be tragic can be comic for them because of their shared community and their new power over their own bodies.

Only a few works make menstruation an important episode, one that defines the character of a woman and her relation to the world around her. Lessing's *The Golden Notebook* participates to a degree in the myth of female irrationality but eventually substitutes a sort of myth of female perspicacity. Erica Jong's *Fear of Flying* creates a new sort of myth with a female hero.

In *The Golden Notebook,* Anna Wulf's notebook entry for September 17, 1954, begins on the morning of her menstruation. Coincidentally, she had earlier decided to "be very conscious of everything" on that particular day—in order to improve her writing.

Lessing then proceeds to lay open Anna's wound. Anna describes her own tension, her irritability, her resentment. She records the "stale smell of menstrual blood," which she feels to be "an imposition from outside." She worries about the odor; she needs her co-worker Jack's "You smell lovely" to make her feel at ease and able to manage anything. Although she tries to see herself as a "free woman," she is nonetheless dependent upon male approval.

Her day at work, punctuated by frequent ablutions and changings of tampons, includes a quarrel with Jack. "I hear my voice shrill and stop myself. I realize my period has caught up with me; there's a moment in every month when it does, and then I get irritated, because it makes me feel helpless and out of control."

Anna's menstrual period also parallels moments of great change in her life. She decides she must leave the Communist party and thinks about the decision while washing herself between her legs. Because of her heightened sensitivity, she realizes that her lover Michael is leaving her.

Menstruation can be seen, then, as a sign of increased awareness of one's identity as a woman. During Anna's menstruation, she is stripped of the relationships that had defined her in others' terms: as part of the party, as part of Michael's life. But Anna's menstruation also makes her both resentful and dependent; she had wanted Michael to love her that night, to take away "the resentment against the wound inside my body which I didn't choose to have."

In *The Golden Notebook*, Lessing communicates a variety of attitudes toward menstruation: disgust, confusion, irritability, resentment, helplessness, alienation. Lessing is a woman giving candid expression to many women's ambivalent feelings about their periods. Anna is both more irrational and more intuitive. Both of these are, after all, qualities generally attributed to women; but in expressing both of them, Lessing allows for the emergence of a more complex mythic view of menstruation.

Jong's *Fear of Flying*, probably the most controversial neofeminist novel, involves menstruation in a reworking of the motif of the hero's quest, the pattern of Joyce's *Ulysses*. As critic Joseph Campbell describes it in *The Hero with a Thousand Faces*, the hero (Odysseus, Aeneas, or whoever) follows certain prescribed steps in his quest: departure from the world he knows in response to a call to adventure; initiation, usually involving temptation by a beautiful woman and a descent to the underworld; and return to his original starting point. Along the way, he gains self-knowledge and knowledge about the past, present, or future of other heroes like himself. We use the term *he* for the hero specifically, not generically; Campbell does not say that women can quest.

But Isadora Wing, Jong's protagonist, does follow the pattern of the male heroic quest. Isadora is called to adventure: a jaunt around Europe with a man other than her husband, from whom she separates herself. Like the hero Theseus, she goes through a labyrinth: a maze of pointless wanderings around Europe with her newfound lover, who plays the role of the temptress, like Circe. When her lover leaves her and she is alone, she has her psychological descent to the underworld: a dark night of the soul in which she reaches inside herself to puzzle out her destiny. She returns to her husband at the end of her quest: a quest that (like those of the male heroes) means a growth in self-knowledge.

But what is also significant is that at the time she decides to return from her descent, she gets her period (something Odysseus never did). The menstruation is part of her identity as female; finding her identity means finding herself as a strong person and a strong woman. When Isadora takes a bath in the last scene, simulating waters of rebirth and resurrection, she looks down and sees "the Tampax string fishing the water like a Hemingway hero" (the materials of female culture are as heroic as those of the male).

Jong shows that menstruation is not "the curse"; rather, it is a kind of blessing on the returning hero. Like Anna Wulf, Isadora Wing experiences acutely the modern woman's conflict: the competition between the claims of independence and love. Both Lessing and Jong use menstruation as a vehicle for showing women's expanding consciousness of themselves. For Anna Wulf and Isadora Wing are most rational—if by rationality we mean both reason and intuition —when they are most womanly.

Part Five

· · · · · · · · · · · · · · · · ·

THE MENOPAUSE

· · · · · · · · · · · · · · ·

Chapter 20

FROM LEECHES TO ESTROGEN: THE MENOPAUSE AND MEDICAL OPTIONS

Menopause (from the Greek words for "month" and "cessation") marks the end of the menstrual flow. The word is sometimes used interchangeably with the broader term *climacteric* (from the Greek words meaning "rung of the ladder" and "critical time"). The climacteric refers to the few years before and after the actual cessation of bleeding and encompasses all the physical and emotional symptoms a woman may experience around the time her periods stop. Other expressions for the menopause are *change of life, critical time, the change, the dangerous age,* and *the dodging time.* The menopause is the last phase of the menstrual cycle. As with every other aspect of menstruation, the same old taboos appear among both primitives and psychoanalysts regarding the menopause.

Menstruation stops when the ovaries cease functioning. One authority has suggested that women stop bleeding when the ovaries have exhausted their egg supply,[1] an unlikely explanation because a newborn girl comes equipped with over half a million eggs. Another doctor thinks that a reduction in the graafian follicles (egg sacs) causes the ovaries to stop functioning.[2] It is known, however, that the cessation in ovarian activity means a sharp reduction in the supply of estrogen, the female sex hormone, and it is the loss of estrogen that causes many of the more noticeable symptoms and side effects of the climacteric.

The average American woman stops menstruating around the age of 50, although menopause can occur normally at any time between the ages of 40 and 60. A century ago, age at menopause could not have been a subject for scientific investigation; average life expectancy was low, and the majority of European and American women did not live to experience menopause. This fact did not prevent widespread speculation about what race or class of women would menstruate the longest. The results and prejudices are similar to those involved in speculations about age at menarche. One doctor thought that "Red Indian" women menstruate beyond the age of 50 but that for "the teeming millions of Chinese" the end of the cycle comes before the fortieth year.[3] Today, the American woman, with an average life expectancy of 75, is likely to outlive her ovaries by about twenty-five years.

Premature menopause (menopause before the age of 40) is experienced by about 8 percent of all women. Perhaps the earliest case on record is the age of 9. One nineteenth-century gynecologist reported the case of a "Hungarian Jewess, fat from her youth," who had her first menstruation at the age of 9, was married at 15½, and went through the menopause at the age of 17.[4]

Explanations for age at menopause reflect the assumptions of the male "experts" who offer them. One nineteenth-century physician said that bad news could bring on an early menopause. He relates the unfortunate story of Elizabeth C., who stopped menstruating at the age of 30 when, one day as she was nursing her baby, her husband dropped dead at her feet. The mother's milk "turned to water," and her periods never returned.[5]

In the same century, a Dr. Andrew Currier explained that "irregular and unwomanly occupations" could cause an early menopause. Those workers most in danger were fishwives, metalworkers, day laborers, cooks, and laundresses. "Surely this is not woman's work," wrote the doctor, "or we would not see such pitiful spectacles of decrepit and wrinkled and worn-out creatures at a period when the blush should still be on their cheeks." Cooks, he thought, had an early menopause from overeating; laundresses, from being exposed to high temperatures. Other causes for premature menopause, said the same doctor, were alcohol, poverty, opium, typhoid, and "excessive sexual indulgence." [6] Dr. Currier's speculations express the moral and class biases of a comfortable Victorian paterfamilias in his speculations. To this day, there is no proven correlation between a woman's menopausal age and her socioeconomic class. Premature menopause is almost always the result of a hormonal imbalance, whether natural or surgically induced.

So, too, those women who remain fertile into their nineties owe that pleasure or pain to the levels of estrogen being produced in their bodies rather than to sexual restraint or working conditions. The oldest age at menopause on record is 104. If we take the title of hormone advocate Robert A. Wilson's book at face value, then 104 is not a very remarkable age at all; women can be, he claims, *Feminine Forever*.[7]

MENOPAUSAL SYMPTOMS
AND ASSOCIATED ILLNESSES

The most common physical symptom of the climacteric is irregular menstrual flow. Another is hot flashes: sensations of warmth in the upper chest and face, often followed by perspiration and chills. Doctors differ on how many women have significant menopausal symptoms. One says 25 percent; the author of *Feminine Forever* says 85 percent.

The Victorian gynecoloist Edward Tilt decreed that a major difficulty of the climacteric was a gradual "loss of feminine grace." At change of life, women begin to look "masculine," their bones either stick out or are sunken in fat, their skin gets flabby, and "tweezers are sometimes required to remove stray hairs from the face.[8] In *Feminine Forever*, Wilson gives much the same portrait. Especially grim is Wilson's description of postmenopausal breasts (he calls breasts "psychological organs," so important are they to a woman's sense of self-esteem):

> After menopause, when estrogen and progesterone sink to a low level, the breasts begin to shrivel and sag. Once the supply of these two nourishing hormones is cut off, the breasts become pendulous, wrinkled, and flabby. Often the skin of the breasts coarsens and is covered with scales. The breasts lose their erotic sensitivity and sometimes do not respond to pain stimuli. Only timely estrogen replacement therapy can prevent this premature decline of a woman's symbol of femininity.

Breast flab is not all women have to look forward to. Among other blessings of the climacteric Wilson lists a "stiff and unyielding" vagina, aching joints, palpitating organs, frequent urination, itching skin, loss of memory, the inability to concentrate, and dryness of the mouth, nose, and eyes.[9] Another doctor observes that menopausal women are often allergic to detergents and to certain kinds of floor polishes.[10]

Some researchers have associated the menopause with bone decalcification, high cholesterol, high blood pressure, and heart disease. But the disease that women fear most, one that has been associated with the menopause since Galen, is cancer.

Popular books and magazine articles almost always warn the menopausal woman that irregular bleeding, particularly any marked increase in the flow, may be a sign of cancer. We are conditioned to think that irregularity means malignancy. Although it is indeed prudent for any person, regardless of age or sex, to be aware of the danger signals of cancer, the dwelling on cancer during the menopause can compound a woman's negative attitude toward aging. Among the 100 women whom Bernice Neugarten interviewed about menopausal attitudes, only 4 saw the end of their periods as a problem of the menopause, but many mentioned the fear of cancer.[11]

Most of us know women who have developed cancer of the breast, cervix, or uterus at a time in their lives that coincided with the menopause. The average age for the menopause for American women is 49; the peak period for cancer of the cervix is 48.[12] The highest incidence of cancer of the ovary, a difficult disease to detect, occurs between the ages of 55 and 65. Wilson sees the uterus as a "possible breeding ground for cancer," but one that can be controlled through estrogen and hysterectomy. Wilson looks forward to the day when hysterectomy will be accepted as a "general preventive route." "If your uterus has been removed," Wilson writes, "estrogen therapy will provide all its benefits without the annoyance of menstrual bleeding. You are a lucky woman indeed." [13]

THE LUCKY WOMAN, OR SEEING THE DOCTOR ABOUT THE MENOPAUSE

A lucky (i.e., wealthy) woman living in London in the 1850s could, if she had the courage to talk about intimate problems with a male doctor, make an appointment with Edward Tilt. Tilt had a wide range of solutions to the problem of menopause, among them mineral water, morphine, syrup of iron and potassium, exercise, traveling, bandaging of limbs, sedatives, and abdominal belts. His preferred method of treatment, however, was bleeding (general venesection). Tilt reasoned that although many women grew stronger during the menopause because their bodies used up the nutrition in the unexpelled blood, many others suffered from the body's failure to dispose of it. Severe headaches were a sign that the woman was storing up the excess blood in her head; if her arm were bled, the unneeded blood would leave the body and her well-being would be restored. Tilt also liked applying leeches—to the anus in the case of hemorrhoids but behind the ears or at the nape of the neck for menopausal disorders. Bleeding was a widely recommended procedure in the nineteenth century for many ailments; it was particularly useful for the menopause, Tilt argued, because it was an "imitation of nature." Tilt's bleeding of twelve ounces of blood from the arm of a 51-year-old patient is alleged to have reduced her dizziness, flushes, and perspiration.[14]

A woman consulting the American gynecologist Andrew Currier in the 1890s would have been told that leeches were still an effective remedy for congested genitals but that venesection was old-fashioned and ineffectual. In his book *The Menopause*, Currier attacked those physicians (such as Tilt) who frightened women with their negative attitudes toward the menopause and who were, in Currier's words, "bleeders, pukers, and purgers." The great cure, according to Currier, was not bleeding but surgery. Riding on the wave of progress evoked by Robert Battey's invention of "female castration" in 1872, Currier proclaimed its merits in the treatment of the menopause. He advocated "artificial menopause": the removal of any organ that directly affects the menstrual process. Be thorough, he advised his colleagues. If you remove the fallopian tubes, then you might as well remove the ovaries, too, because without the tubes the ovarian function is gone. Remove the *whole* ovary instead of just part of one, and remove the ovaries in the case of any new growth, benign or malignant. Of course, one always stumbled across the rare patient for whom surgery offered no salvation: "This would include some who had long been subject to vicious habits, to the use of alcohol, chloral, opium, etc." [15]

Currier's method is still highly favored among American doctors. Apparently, 63 percent of American women between the ages of 50 and 64 have had "artificial menopause." [16] The methods may vary, but the end result is the same as it was almost a century ago: the literal castration of the female.

Although surgery is the preferred American technique for destroying the function of a woman's ovaries and her uterus, another is called *radiation menopause*. This controversial treatment can be achieved through X-ray of the pelvic area or through circulating radium in the uterus through a tube. With the latter method, there is said to be a greater risk of uterine cancer. With both methods, there are some unpleasant side effects, including uncontrollable bleeding and loss of sexual desire.

Surgery and radiation are indeed ways to curtail natural menopause. Other modern proposals for cheating nature have been monkey gland transplants and injections of the cells of an unborn lamb. One doctor has ironically suggested "grafting 'young' ovaries into menopausal women" as a way to eliminate the process of aging.[16] But the most widely acclaimed "cure" for the menopause, the one that made headlines in 1966, is estrogen-replacement therapy.

ESTROGEN THERAPY

The two female hormones that affect the menstrual cycle are estrogen and progesterone, which are produced by certain cells of the ovaries and possibly by the adrenal glands. The decrease in estrogen levels brings on the menopause, although some researchers say that 40 percent of all women maintain moderate hormonal activity even after the menopause.

Estrogen was first isolated in 1923 by Allen and Doisey. It is the general name for three collective hormones (estradiol, estrone, and estriol) that are converted into usable substances in the liver. To make his first drop of estrogen in the 1920s, Doisey used up the ovaries of 80,000 sows. Another source of natural estrogen is Australian clover, which has been said to make grazing sheep sterile. But the most common source of natural estrogen is the urine of pregnant mares.

Today, most estrogen is produced synthetically and is administered primarily in pill form. There are also some local preparations, prescribed for women who cannot take estrogen orally. These creams help to restore the vaginal tissue; their primary deficiency is that they are too easily absorbed. Another form of estrogen, not currently in wide use but destined to be if the present trend continues, is a hormone pellet implanted under the buttocks. One English doctor who recommends this treatment says that the implantation method is superior to all others: It is weaker than a daily dosage; the hormones are not apt to lose their effectiveness in the liver; there is no way of affecting the stomach or intestines; there is little risk of embolism; and there is the psychological advantage of not having to think about taking medicine. This very optimistic physician has had excellent results with the more than 1,000 women he has treated. Like Wilson, he sees estrogen therapy as a revolutionary discovery that will retard the aging process.[17]

Others have been less optimistic, less willing to proclaim estrogen as the elixir of youth. The drug has had many reported side effects, including a high incidence of heart disease and blood clotting. Synthetic estrogens, particularly the substance known as *diethylstilbestrol* (DES), have been linked with cancer. Other synthetic estrogens have been connected with liver disturbances and shifts in blood-sugar levels.

Defenders of estrogen therapy have answered these charges. Huggins, for example, won a Nobel Prize for discovering that oral contraceptives (which contain estrogen and progesterone) are more likely to reduce cancer than cause it. Wilson, in his more than twenty-seven years of prescribing estrogen for menopausal women, had not a single woman develop cancer, although the odds were that 18 of the 304 women would contract the disease. As we write this (1976), convincing evidence is beginning to appear that links excessive estrogen therapy with an increased risk of cancer.

The choice of estrogen therapy must be a highly individual one. We think all women should educate themselves about this issue so that they can make intelligent individual decisions when the choice becomes necessary. All women should visit a gynecologist for an annual checkup and Pap smear; it might be a good idea to make an annual visit to a medical library as well. There is no waiting in line, and the service is free. The reference book called *Biological Abstracts* contains, under the category "Menopause," a summary of the medical findings for that year on that topic. It is not too difficult to learn what is being said about the menopause and by whom.

The more technical essays tend to avoid the kind of rhetoric that characterizes Wilson's book. For the main fault of *Feminine Forever* lies not in the medicine but in the moralizing. Wilson's insistent theme is that women are delightful creatures whose beauty must be preserved. Each man, he argues, marries an Aphrodite or a Helen of Troy. The sensitive doctor is the one who keeps Helen glowing through the dismal years of her middle age. "A woman's physical appeal is her starting capital in the venture of life—the 'ante' which lets her into the game," Wilson writes in defense of his theory.

One gynecologist told us that Wilson's reputation in medical circles has suffered because of his evangelical approach to estrogen therapy for all. The fact is, all women in their climacteric do not require estrogen therapy. The ones who do, get it from their doctors as needed. No competent or honorable gynecologist, face to face with an anxious 49-year-old woman, would dare to promise eternal youth as Wilson does from the safety of the printed page.

In the foreword to *Feminine Forever*, Dr. Greenblatt praises his colleague: "Like a gallant knight he has come to rescue his fair lady not at the time of her bloom and flowering but in her despairing years; at a time of her life when the preservation and prolongation of her femaleness are so paramount." But in emphasizing a woman's breasts and legs rather than her intelligence or skills, the gallant knight reinforces the most destructive stereotypes in our sexist society.

Nor can we be thoroughly convinced, as Wilson is, that estrogen therapy is woman's salvation. What seems true in one age can be judged folly in another. Edward Tilt had the most knightly of intentions, surely, when he sapped away his menopausal patients' strength by removing the blood from arms, in imitation of nature. To thumb one's nose at Mother Nature now, during the estrogen craze, would be a disservice to those women who have little need either for hormone replacement or for identification with Aphrodite.

Chapter 21

. . . .

PSYCHOLOGY AND
THE MENOPAUSAL MENACE

Victorian medicine men knew in their hearts that during the menopause, a woman could expect to have mental problems. According to Dr. Edward Tilt, the change-of-life woman was susceptible to certain mental "diseases," among them "morbid irrationality," "minor forms of hysteria," melancholia, and the impulses to drink spirits, to steal, and perchance, to murder.[1] Freud, although he did not see the menopause as a disease, nonetheless thought it to be a stage of potential crisis, a time when previously undisturbed women could become neurotic. Often, said Freud, menopausal women "become quarrelsome and obstinate, petty and stingy, show typical sadistic and anal-erotic features which they did not show before."[2]

Freud's occasional perceptions of the menopause, like his comments on the menarche, were fully developed by the analyst Helene Deutsch. Deutsch viewed the menopause as the "third edition" of the infantile stage, the second being the menarche. During both of these traumatic times, she argued, women act out certain unconscious fantasies. The first menstruation is fraught with fears of castration and lost children; the last is filled with fantasies of rape and prostitution. Her theory that the menarche is the moment at which a woman becomes the "servant of the species" justifies her view of the menopause as the stage at which the woman's service to the species ends.[3] The woman becomes biologically useless; she can have no more children. Here is another instance of psychoanalysts converting the complaints of a few women seeking psychiatric help into a universal theory of female sexuality. The medical-psychiatric community considers the menarche, menstruation, and now the menopause "conditions" to be treated, and their theories of treatment spill over into definitions of the normally functioning woman.

Deutsch's influence can be seen in the writings of other analysts and popularizers of psychoanalytic ideas. Eric Erickson, for example, writes that when a woman's womb is "empty" she experiences pain. Her grief for lost children, reiterated at each menstruation, becomes during the menopause "a permanent scar." [4] Joseph Rheingold, in *The Fear of Being a Woman,* relates the menopause to his theory of maternal destructiveness. The menopause is a traumatic event, accompanied by an "isolation by loss," the loss of the childbearing capacity. "Some women make a career of the menopause," claims Rheingold.[5]

How do these dismissed servants of the race behave during their menopausal years? Well, writes one doctor, unless they have the right outlet, menopausal women are apt to become *"mischief makers,* developing a heightened interest in their married sons and daughters and often becoming a great menace as meddlesome mothers-in-law." [6] The menacing mother-in-law is a major stereotype for the menopausal woman; another is the television addict. Morton Hunt, in a book entitled, inappropriately, *Her Infinite Variety,* has a rather one-dimensional idea about the menopausal type. She is foolish and what people call "typically feminine." Her time is spent pursuing astrologists and palm readers, writing letters to advice columnists, watching television, playing bridge, and making "lemming-like migrations to see visiting movie stars." [7]

Philip Wylie's menacing mom, the American Cinderella gone to flab, exhibits "caprices" that Wylie labels "menopausal": "These caprices are of a menopausal nature at best—hot flashes, rage, infantilism, weeping, sentimentality, peculiar appetite." [8] In *The Second Sex,* Simone de Beauvoir also presents a momish portrait of the menopausal woman, although she places her middle-class menace more clearly within a cultural context than Wylie does. Because woman lives in a patriarchal culture where she is denied selfhood, argues de Beauvoir, she will inevitably behave in an infantile manner. Relying on both Deutsch and Wylie as sources, de Beauvoir describes the menopausal woman in rather negative terms. Denied identity by the male society, she retreats to infantile fantasies of what might have been. At the verge of a new independence, the menopausal woman will usually reject it. "She babbles to men in a childish voice and with naïve glances of admiration, and she chatters on about when she was a little girl: she chirps instead of talking, she claps her hands, she bursts out laughing." Some women may revive their abandoned dreams of playing the piano or painting pictures; others become willing dupes of religious or spiritualist happiness peddlers. Restless, irritable, tormented by the flesh, she is likely to seek the attention of young men and will, in fact, buy that attention if it does not come freely. Finished and outdated in a culture that has no use for her, the menopausal woman tyrannizes over her sons and daughters, even promoting the daughter's abortion in order to keep the privilege of maternity to herself. Some women, says de Beauvoir, bless the appearance of a war or a famine, for then their knitting will be needed.

Of all menopausal women, says the French philosopher, it is the American who is the worst. She must agree with Wylie that the American mom cannot think or read, knows nothing of science or art. De Beauvoir goes so far as to blame the American woman for the decline of literature: best sellers are written for the American mom market, "to entertain idle women in search of escape." [9]

Fortunately for the future of the race, some writers give more humane and realistic assessments of the "menopausal personality." The analyst Clara Thompson, for one, thinks the menopause is a threat primarily to two distinct types of women: "those who have postponed living until too late and those who have managed to maintain a feeling of importance and value only through the adulation of men." [10] Most of the hazards of the menopause are culturally induced. Thompson reports the fact that among Chinese women, there are almost no menopausal problems because older women in China are given power and respect as they reach maturity. The psychoanalyst George Devereux has noted similar circumstances among Mohave women. In that society, the menopause is a sign of achievement; Mohave women are free to work, to flirt, and to be wise during their middle years.[11] In overemphasizing the plight of the white American woman of the middle class, de Beauvoir neglects this broader cultural view.

Today, a more common theme is the menopause as "rebirth," a time when woman is freed from childbearing and child rearing, freed to a new enjoyment of sex and a renewed dedication to her work. Women writing about themselves have actually sounded this note throughout history, but it seems to have been ignored by the clinicians.

The suffragist Eliza Farnham, writing in the 1860s, saw menopause as a time of "secret joy," of spiritual growth, of "super-exaltation." She attributed the negative attitudes toward menopause to "masculine errors." [12] Anna Garlin Spencer, an American writer of the early twentieth century, found in the change of life a new freedom. Released from the ties of home and childbearing, the woman in her middle years can have a life "as 'straight' as man's, and the 'curves' that had required consideration at their weakest point are no longer a part of her existence." [13] Clelia Mosher, the author of *Health and the Woman Movement,* claimed that women are *taught* to dread the menopause. Yet, those women who are "busy and useful," who have "absorbing occupations," have little to worry about.[14]

More recent testimonies indicate that if a woman has a positive attitude toward the menopause, this stage of life need not be a threat. Seven California women, most of them postmenopausal, spoke on video tape of their feelings during the climacteric. Only two had experienced any anxiety in the menopause. One of the women found menopause to be a "liberation," a more "joyful" time than she had had in the preceding twenty years.[15] The 100 women in the Neugarten study were generally happy about their own menopause. One woman said, "I'm so happy about not menstruating any more, I could dance with joy. I was looking forward to it for years." [16]

No longer bound to their rhythms or their families, post-menopausal women are freed from any of the social and biological restrictions that the patriarchy imposes on their lives. They have no need for baby-sitters or birth control. They are in the position to establish, perhaps for the first time in their lives, a separate identity. Many women celebrate this new liberty with a divorce. Others, however, discover a renewed sexual life with their long-term mates.

For it is a myth that with the end of the menstrual cycle comes an end to sexual desire. Some, it is true, may use the menopause as an excuse for sexual denial, but only those women who never liked sex in the first place. A thirty-three-year-old woman who went through premature menopause was very much worried that her sexual appeal would diminish. But her doctor sagely remarked: "Men don't marry us for our periods, you know." When she told her husband the bad news that they would soon be unable to have any more children, he answered: "But honey, we weren't seriously thinking about having any more, anyway." Her husband's tenderness and understanding, plus the decreasing need for contraceptive devices, made their sexual relationship "more satisfying than ever." [17]

Extremists in the past have predicted either complete frigidity or uncontrollable nymphomania as the sexual response to the menopause. However, a number of recent studies show that there is very little change in sexual attitude for the majority of women during the climacteric. Some of Thompson's patients continued to have a strong sex life into their seventies. The majority of women in Neugarten's study found little or no change in their sexual attitudes as they entered the menopause; of the thirty-five women who did experience a change, they were equally divided on whether sex got better or worse. Neugarten and some other current investigators have concluded that it is *not* physiological change but rather the cultural attitude toward aging which creates depression or negative self-concepts in menopausal women.

As women gain increased control of their own bodies, as

they continue to talk to each other about menstruation, the menopause, and other socially tabooed topics, they will help to clear away some of the misconceptions about female sexuality. There is much in print concerning the menopausal menace. Perhaps this is because women, silenced for so long, have had too many "authorities" describe them. But women's stories exist—in letters, in journals, in unpublished manuscripts. In these documents, as in the published works of many, are to be found the women who have been too busy or too committed to flock to movie houses or the arms of adolescent men. As their lives are made public, the menopausal menace shall, like the mom and the mother-in-law, resume her human and unmenacing dimensions.

. . . .

"NOVEMBER OF THE BODY": THE MENOPAUSE AND LITERATURE

Until the last quarter of the nineteenth century, the word *menopause* did not exist in the English language. Andrew Marvell and Sir Thomas Browne, English writers of the seventeenth century, had used the word *climacter* to indicate a critical stage in a man's life, but not in a woman's. The sexual decline of a woman's body, generally called *change of life*, was not a significant theme in British or American literature until the twentieth century.

The absence of women's voices from the centuries-old record of the human experience must surely be responsible for this void in literature. On the other hand, there are countless references to old age in European literature, from the Greeks to the moderns. The process of aging was a concern of Euripides, Shakespeare, Donne, Hugo, Tolstoy, Baudelaire, T. S. Eliot. Even Simone de Beauvoir, in *The Coming of Age,* although she provides a thorough analysis of the theme of old age in literature, gives no specific attention to woman's change of life. We shall try to fill in the record here.

One of the earliest and most introspective writers on the fear of reproductive decay was Elizabeth Barrett Browning. In a letter written to Robert Browning during their courtship, Elizabeth Barrett warned her fiancé that marrying her would be like emptying his "water gourds into the sand." The sand suggests dryness or absence of fluid, the sterility of the womb. Her famed *Sonnets from the Portuguese*, written shortly before the elopement, show similar fears of barrenness. Elizabeth Barrett was then thirty-nine years old, too old, she feared, for a fruitful marriage. She describes herself in images of dust, ashes, decay. In Sonnet 18 she remarks that her youth is gone:

> My days of youth went yesterday;
> My hair no longer bounds to my foot's glee,
> Nor plant I it from rose or myrtle-tree,
> As girls do, any more:

In Sonnet 4 she compares her body to a dilapidated house: "Look up and see the casement broken in, / The bats and owlets builders in the roof!" Elizabeth Barrett is communicating, in these premarital sonnets, a dread of her approaching change of life; but, in fact, she was not sterile. She bore one son and suffered four miscarriages during her marriage, the last being her most serious illness since leaving England for the healthier climate of Italy.[1]

The desire for a child is strong in the menopause of Joanna Burden, Joe Christmas's mistress in Faulkner's *Light in August:* "It was as if she knew somehow that time was short, that autumn was almost upon her, without knowing yet the exact significance of autumn." Like Anne Sexton's "November of the body," Joanna Burden's autumn signifies the ending of fertility, the last chance for bearing a child. Miss Burden tells Joe Christmas that she is pregnant. But her body has lied. In his shame and disgust, Christmas strikes her, calling her an old woman. "You haven't got any baby," he said. "You never had one. There is not anything the matter with you except being old. You just got old and it happened to you and now you are not any good any more." The unnamed *it* is, of course, the menopause.

Some menopausal women in literature who want a child meet a happier fate than Joanna Burden did. The Old Testament, for example, records the story of Sarah, the barren wife of Abraham, who, though old, "conceived, and bare Abraham a son [Isaac] in his old age, at the set time of which God had spoken to him" (Genesis 21:2).

There is a parallel legend in the New Testament in the Book of Luke. Zacharias and Elisabeth, both "now well stricken in years," have no child (1:7). But an angel comes to Zacharias telling him that the barren wife will bear a son, to be named John. When the angel comes to Mary to announce the blessedness of her womb, he informs Mary that Elisabeth, her cousin, has also conceived a son: "And this is the sixth month with her, who was called barren. For with God nothing shall be impossible" (1:36–37). Shortly afterward, Mary visits her cousin: "When Elisabeth heard the salutation of Mary, the babe leaped in her womb" (1:41).

In both of these stories from the Bible, it is the Lord, not the mothers, who are primarily responsible for the conceptions. In both, a son is born, not a daughter. The birth of a son is the wish granted to an Irish peasant woman in Jack London's story "Samuel." But in London's story, the menopausal pregnancy is seen by the people as the work of the devil rather than the work of God.

Margaret Henan, the central character of "Samuel," is the mother of six sons and six daughters. But the sons named Samuel, in honor of Margaret's brother, do not survive. After the third Samuel's death by drowning, Margaret bears, at the age of forty-seven, still another Samuel, whom she must take to another town to christen, so frightened are the people at this point of Margaret's name choosing. One woman tells the narrator: "She was forty-seven, I'm tellun' ye, and she had a child ot forty-seven. Thunk on ut! Ot forty-seven! Ut was fair scand'lous." The baby is born an "eediot." Disturbed by his fourth Samuel's braying, the father kills the child and then himself. Without the father, Margaret is unable to conceive a fifth Samuel.

This story, supposedly a legend of McGill Island, is told from the point of view of a stranger to the island. As a detached observer, he is able to admire Margaret's strength and self-determination. For the natives, however, Margaret is a threat, a witchlike woman who is in touch with the devil and whose moribund fertility brings destruction.

In *Hamlet*, the sexual corruption and lack of judgment

that make something rotten in the state of Denmark seem to emanate from a middle-aged woman. Gertrude has a characteristic observable in other change-of-life women in literature, what her son calls "an increase of appetite." Hamlet, furious that his mother has remarried immediately after the death of his father, generalizes that fury: "Frailty, thy name is woman!" (Act 1, Scene 2). In the confrontation scene in Gertrude's bedroom (Act 3, Scene 4), Hamlet condemns his mother for not acting her age:

> You cannot call it love, for at your age
> The heyday in the blood is tame, it's humble
> And waits upon the judgment.

Here again, Hamlet makes a general statement about female nature from his own philosophical presupposition, then goes on to say that with such mutiny in a "matron's bones," we can hardly expect virtue from youth. Gertrude's menopausal passion is responsible for the dissolution of the family and the collapse of the state.

The majority of mutinous matrons in literature confine their destructiveness to the smaller unit. They suffer and complain, threatening their sons and daughters and husbands and, of course, themselves. For example, Alma, the doting white mother of Lillian Smith's novel *Strange Fruit*, finds it difficult to control either her children or herself during the menopause. *"Change of life makes you like that.* She must not permit herself to go to pieces over something trivial." F. Scott Fitzgerald, so often in search of a simple explanation for his wife Zelda's misbehavior, found a perfect one in the menopause; Fitzgerald even asked Zelda's doctor to discuss the mother's menopausal imbalance with Scottie, their daughter.

In John O'Hara's last novel, *The Ewings*, Ada's son and daughter-in-law speculate about the effects of the menopause on Ada's behavior. Edna has heard a lot of talk about menopause that she passes on to her husband: "You stop menstruating, and have these hot flashes, and I *have* heard that you lose all sexual desire, but on the other hand, I've heard that when it's over your sexual desire is as great as ever." Some women, Edna continues, get depressed or even "suicidal."

Kate Brown, the heroine of Doris Lessing's novel *The Summer Before the Dark,* has, like Ada Ewing, some offspring terribly concerned about their mother's menopause. Kate's children start treating her in a "humorous and indulgent" manner, assuming that she's going through the change of life. They treat the mother like "an invalid" and her stray cats like "medicine." One day, Kate overhears the children talking about the cat: "Just the thing for the menopause," they say.

In the case of Gertrude in *Hamlet,* the menace is the woman herself. In the domestic situations described by Lessing and O'Hara, however, the real menace seems to be the children, who attempt to define, as indeed Hamlet did with Gertrude, their mothers' behavior.

A number of fictional characters experience the menopause alone, without husbands or children. For Mrs. Stone of Tennessee Williams's *The Roman Spring of Mrs. Stone* and Mrs. Eliot of Angus Wilson's *The Middle Age of Mrs. Eliot,* the menopause coincides with widowhood. Mrs. Stone experiences three critical events in the same year: the abandonment of her career, the death of her husband, and "that interval of a woman's life when the ovarian cycle is cut off." At first, Mrs. Stone is depressed and "unfocused"; at the end of what Williams calls the "moon of pause," however, she temporarily discovers a new life and new energy. Although Angus Wilson is less graphic about Meg Eliot's menopause, he nonetheless gives his forty-three-year-old heroine certain characteristics usually associated with that stage: a lack of purpose, a tendency toward headaches and crying spells, a feeling of barrenness, "like an old virgin afraid of turning sour." The widow is on the brink of psychic disintegration until, aided by her brother, she works her way back into the world.

MENOPAUSE AND DEATH

For some women, the problems and anxieties of the climacteric are insurmountable. Hamlet's mother's wantonness leads to her destruction and to the deaths of her son, her lover, and quite a few others. Mrs. Stone, who becomes after the "moon of pause" a woman of passion, is eventually discarded by her young Italian lover. In the last scene of the novel, she throws her keys to a sinister gigolo who has been following her for months, thus openly inviting him to rob and perhaps murder her. Joanna Burden, rejected by Joe Christmas because he finds her old and useless, plans a suicide pact with him. Christmas, however, runs from the burning house after Miss Burden shoots herself. He is eventually lynched.

At times, the menopause is associated with death by cancer. When she meets an acquaintance she doesn't want to see again, Mrs. Stone invents the story that she had had her uterus removed but that the cancer has spread. Telling the lie gives Karen Stone a feeling of liberation, of having arrived at the "void." Her lie becomes the truth, of course, at the end of the novel. The cancer is a moral one, the final loss of dignity; the "void" is sexual abandon and ultimately death.

Molly Bloom, the aging wife in Joyce's *Ulysses*, is menstruating near the end of the novel. She notices that her periods have become irregular: "Is there anything the matter with my insides or have I something growing in me getting that thing like that every week when was it last Whit Monday yes its only about three weeks I ought to go to the doctor." "That thing" is her period, come again after only three weeks. She worries that something is the matter with her "insides," that there might be "something growing" in her. The worry is probably the fear of cancer.

But the most unusual connection between the menopause and cancer appears in Thomas Mann's novel *The Black Swan*. In that story a middle-aged mother, a woman of feeling, goes on a journey with her daughter, a woman of reason. The mother falls in love with the young guide who takes them on a tour of a damp cave. In her sexual excitement, the mother, Rosalie, begins to bleed. She rejoices that the cycle has reasserted itself, calling her new blood "my visitation—this Easter of my womanhood." Instead, the blood signals carcinoma of the uterus.

MENOPAUSE AND REBIRTH

Women who threaten themselves or their families during the menopause often do so in response to the fear that they may lose their sexual desirability. A character in Betty Smith's

A Tree Grows in Brooklyn regrets that she has had so few lovers now that the menopause is approaching and "soon all her woman-ness will be lost." In a poem called "Two" from *Pro Femina,* Carolyn Kizer taunts those women who invest everything in their looks: "You can wait for the menopause, and catch up on your reading." But nowhere is the disappearance of a woman's sex appeal at the menopause more brutally stated than in Henry Miller's *Tropic of Cancer.* "If she were only ten years younger!" complains Carl to Henry.

> If she were only ten years younger I might overlook the streak of grey hair . . . and even the brittle arms. But she's too old. You see, with a cunt like that every year counts now. . . . She said she was turning forty. That means fifty or sixty. It's like fucking your own mother . . . you can't do it . . . it's impossible.

In this passage, Miller captures, in livelier language to be sure, the brittle, saggy, unyielding female who Robert Wilson in *Feminine Forever* warns us we will someday become if we don't take estrogen.

However, not all women in literature turn brittle or lose their sexual drive at the menopause, nor even their appeal to men. Molly Bloom, in her middle age, is still an Andalusian flower. After menopause Mrs. Stone, no longer subject to the "red tides," finds that, with the danger of pregnancy gone, she is capable of "desire and its possible gratification." She feels no physical deterioration following the menopause. "On the contrary, now that her body was rising out of the tangled woods of the climacteric, she felt a great resurgence of physical well-being." Unfortunately, the new energy leads her to the wrong man, a younger version of Henry Miller's friend Carl, a man who makes his living servicing women. It is the lover's rejection of her that causes Mrs. Stone's degeneration.

Some of the women in fiction who pull through the change with renewed vigor do so without relating sexually to a man. Meg Eliot of Angus Wilson's novel recovers after being nursed by her homosexual brother. She recovers and eventually leaves him to become the personal secretary of a woman member of parliament. The heroine of May Sarton's novel *Mrs. Stevens Hears the Mermaids Singing* experiences nothing that Ms. Sarton calls the menopause. But at the age of forty-five, Mrs. Stevens finds a new Muse, Dorothea, and from this relationship Mrs. Stevens creates new art. Ada Ewing, the main character of O'Hara's *The Ewings*, discovers sexual rebirth and a new life at the age of fifty-two. She masturbates for the first time and enjoys it. She also has an affair with a younger woman but eventually leaves town and goes to the West Coast to live with a woman her own age, leaving behind the son and daughter-in-law who had been so concerned that she would be suicidal or depressed during the menopause.

But the two best-known symbols in literature for menopausal renewal have been with us longer than Ada Ewing or Molly Bloom. One is Penelope, the character from the *Odyssey* on whom Molly is modeled. Penelope, who waits faithfully for her husband while he fights wars and seduces goddesses, grows old in his absence. When she and Odysseus are reunited, Penelope describes her suffering:

> Think
> what difficulty the gods gave: they denied us life together in our
> prime and flowering years, kept us from crossing into age
> together.

In the reunion, nonetheless, the gods are kind. For Athena makes both husband and wife younger, more attractive, more desirable than either had been during the separation. Both they and Ithaca are restored.

Chaucer's Wife of Bath is a more realistic and less monogamous menopausal model than Penelope. In the course of her very active life, the sensuous Wife wears out five husbands, thus reversing the stereotype of the aging *male* who runs through a series of young mates. "The Wife of Bath's Tale" also has menopausal implications. In that story, a young knight is forced to marry the old hag who saves his life by telling him what women want: mastery over men. On their wedding night, the hero is miserable; he is unable to kiss his wife because she is so "foule," so "lothly and so old," so ill-bred. After a long lecture, the aged wife asks him to choose between a wife who is "foule and old" but humble and a wife who is "yong and fair" but apt to entertain visitors. The knight, in keeping with the spirit of the story, turns the choice over to his wife. Now that she has mastery, she changes into a beautiful and young but faithful wife.

In the world of epics and folktales, menopausal women such as Penelope and the old hag are magically transformed into young women. In real life, there are no such options. Estrogen, the magical substance of our own scientific age, has some of the power of Athena's potion. But estrogen will not take away the wrinkles already there nor straighten bent backs.

The twentieth-century Penelope, Molly Bloom, had neither magic nor synthetic hormones to halt the aging process. Molly's solution was to keep on living, to affirm the power of her womanhood. In her soliloquy, the dominant word is *yes*.

> I love flowers Id love to have the whole place swimming in roses
> . . . yes he said I was a flower of the mountain yes so we are
> flowers all a womans body yes that was one true thing he said in
> his life and the sun shines for you today yes that was why I like
> him because he saw he understood or felt what a woman is . . .
> and first I put my arms around him yes and drew him down to me
> so he could feel my breasts all perfume yes and his heart was
> going like mad and yes I said yes I will Yes!

Molly's monologue occurs while she is menstruating. Although worried about her irregularity and afraid that she should see a doctor, Molly still affirms the flowering and bleeding of her body, aware as she does so of the inevitable wilting. Like the Wife of Bath, she has mastery over herself.

Part Six

. . . .

SIDESHOW

. . . .

Chapter 23

THE MENSTRUAL
HALL OF FAME

On a fancy Long Island beach, a young woman goes for a midnight swim. She is bitten in half by a shark. All that rolls ashore is her head on her shoulders. Later, it's suggested that she had her period, a thing attractive to sharks.

This grisly incident is the trigger for the plot in Peter Benchley's 1974 novel, *Jaws*. A similar real-life event happened in the summer of 1967, in Glacier National Park, Montana. Two young women campers were mauled to death by a grizzly bear. It was later said that one of them had been menstruating and that the smell of blood had enticed the bear.

Probably no famous queens or female leaders have been cut off in midcareer by sharks or grizzly bears, but menstruation has sometimes changed the course of history. If Queen Elizabeth I had menstruated regularly, she might have married, might have had a child and changed the future of the British monarchy. If the seventeenth-century American reformer Anne Hutchinson had not been undergoing menopause at a critical time, she might have given birth to a child rather than the premature deformity that confirmed her enemies' belief that she was a witch. The biblical Salome allegedly suffered from menstrual cramps. Was her request for John the Baptist's head a desire for revenge against the non-menstruators of the human race, a desire to see a man bleed?

Joan of Arc, it is said, never menstruated at all; she was twenty when she was burned at the stake. The eccentric French historian Jules Michelet writes of Joan that "in her the life of the spirit dominated, absorbed the lower life, and held in check its *vulgar infirmities*. . . . She grew up to be robust and handsome; *but the physical curse of women never affected her.*" Although Michelet seems to regard the possibility of Joan's menstruating with disgust, he was fascinated with his own wife's monthly bleedings and recorded them meticulously: date and time of day they began, color and character of the discharge, his feelings (but rarely hers) about the flow. His observations may still be read today in his *Journal*.[1]

For Joan of Arc, lack of periods may have been useful in battle. For Queen Mary I of England (1516–1558) and her younger half sister Elizabeth I (1533–1603), their childlessness (probably due to syphilis inherited from their father, Henry VIII) created great dynastic problems. Queen Mary suffered all her life from "ischomenia" (now called *amenorrhea*, or lack of periods). Without success, she tried all the medical remedies known to her era: bleeding; manus Christi (literally, "the hand of Christ," an exotic mixture of powdered pearls, gold leaf, sugar, and rose water, to be eaten in the morning with the yolk of an egg), and "aqua composita" (a compound of Gascoigne wine, infusion of ginger, galingale, which is another kind of ginger, camomile, cinnamon, nutmeg, grains, cloves, and anise seed). Mary's barrenness, left uncured by these remedies, was a source of great unhappiness to her and a cause of the rift between her and her husband, King Philip II of Spain. Her nickname in history, bestowed because of her fierce persecutions of Protestants, is curiously ironic: Bloody Mary.

The Roman Catholic Mary desperately wanted a child so that the throne would not pass to her Protestant half sister, Elizabeth. But Elizabeth, it turned out, was also childless (she was succeeded by James I, a cousin whose wife bore the necessary son). Elizabeth, known as the Virgin Queen, never married; it is frequently said that she did not want to share her throne with a man. But her periods were infrequent, and it may be that she assumed she was sterile and hence felt no need to legitimize her relationships with the male flatterers who always surrounded her. Or she may have indeed preferred chastity to the possibility of dying in childbirth, which was not uncommon in her era.

Elizabeth became queen in 1558; by the following year, there were many rumors that she was sterile and that her frequent bleedings were intended to remedy her lack of periods. Her laundresses noticed that she had very few monthly periods, and this fact became widely known. In addition to bleedings, Elizabeth also followed the directions of Lord Cecil, her chief adviser: Use only foods and scents "vouched for"; avoid irritant skin poisons by checking carefully anything touching her bare body; keep doors closed where her laundresses and wardrobe women did their work. Elizabeth's regimen was, apparently, no more successful than Mary's.

In seventeenth-century America, it was not uncommon for a woman who behaved improperly—a shrew, a gossip, a religious questioner—to be considered a witch. This was the case of Anne Hutchinson (1591–1643) of Massachusetts, who preached the doctrine of salvation through grace and argued that women should have a voice in church affairs. Because she was successful in medicine (healing herbs) and midwifery, she acquired a ready following for her theological opinions. Mistress Hutchinson was placed on trial for these opinions in 1637.

During this trial, she was pregnant and seriously ill, but she was not allowed to sit down until it was obvious that she could no longer stand; her archenemy, Governor John Winthrop, records unfeelingly that "her countenance discovered some bodily infirmity." [2] Because of her ill health, she was finally broken and unable to carry on her defense; as a result, she was excommunicated and banished from the colony.

Menopausal pregnancy seems to have been the cause of Anne Hutchinson's medical troubles. She suffered from hot flashes and other symptoms. During her menopause, she aborted New England's first hydatidiform (watery) mole. Dr. John Clarke, a physician and preacher, described this "monstrous birth" with grotesque precision. It was "twenty-seven

lumps of man's seed without any alteration or mixture of anything from the woman . . . every one of them greatly confused." The lumps were knit together by strings, which Clarke
believed were the beginnings of veins and nerves and which
were snarled together. The lumps contained "partly wind and
partly water"; six of them were as large as a man's fist, and one
as large as two fists. "The globes were round things included
in the lumps, about the smallness of a small Indian bean, and
like the pearl in a man's eye. The two lumps which differed
from the rest were like liver or congealed blood, and had no
small globes in them as the rest had." [3] This was taken as a
further sign of her being a witch and did not help her case.

Anne Hutchinson's troubles were probably increased by
the psychological stresses of the trial. Queen Marie Antoinette
(1755–1793), anticipating the guillotine, developed traumatic
menstrual bleeding several days before her execution. On that
final day, she had wanted to wear a white dress, the color of
royal mourning, but found her chemise stained with blood.
The gendarme refused to let her out of his sight to change her
clothes, so she crouched in the narrow space between the bed
and the wall, with the kitchen maid standing between her and
the gendarme, to hide her nakedness. She was ashamed to
leave her soiled linen for the prying eyes of those who would
examine her cell after she was gone, so she stuffed her chemise
into a crevice in the wall behind the stove. Her bleeding
served as one of her final punishments.

Emma Goldman, the feminist-anarchist (1869–1940), was
known as "Red Emma the Witch"—but for her politics, not
her periods. Her periods were, however, irregular and painful.
Like Marie Antoinette, she bled as a result of psychological
stress. When her family was being smuggled from Königsberg
in 1881 to escape the pogroms, young Emma's period came
early, "due to the excitement of our departure," she writes in
her autobiography, *Living My Life*. The family had to plunge
through icy water, and Emma says "the sudden chill froze my
blood; then I felt a stinging sensation in my spine, abdomen,
and legs, as if I were being pierced with hot irons." [4] When
they reached their destination, Emma was given hot tea,
packed in hot bricks, and covered with a large feather bed.
She was an invalid for weeks; her spine remained weak for
years afterward.

As an adult, Emma found her periods were still painful and consulted a doctor who suggested an operation that would free her from menstrual pain, allow her to have full sexual pleasure, and enable her to have children. But consulting her political ideals, Emma finally decided to "find an outlet for my mother-need in the love of *all* children." The operation did not take place. Emma devoted her life to writing and political action.

Other women writers have suffered from menstruation. The British poet Elizabeth Barrett Browning (1806–1861) took opium for her cramps and may have become addicted. Olive Schreiner (1855–1920), the South African–British novelist, suffered greatly from premenstrual tension that prevented her from working. She lamented that her friend Eleanor Marx (Karl's daughter) was the only person with whom she could discuss her trouble. The French novelist George Sand (1804–1876) once mistook menstrual pains for a serious fever and later said apologetically to her husband, "I was afraid that I might be threatened with a serious illness, but realize now that this indisposition coincided with the bad time of the month for me." [5] It also coincided with her first adultery.

For the British novelist Virginia Woolf (1882–1941), however, menstruation unleashed the flow of imagination. In her diary entry for February 18, 1928, she records that

> I had thought to write the quickest most brilliant pages in *Orlando* yesterday—not a drop came, all, forsooth, for the usual physical reasons, which delivered themselves today. It is the oddest feeling: as if a finger stopped the flow of the ideas in the brain; it is unsealed and the blood rushes all over the place.[6]

Menstruation, then, is not always an impediment to women. Although it may be an embarrassment or a source of pain, it may also be a liberation, as with Virginia Woolf and with Lizzie Borden, that legendary New England murderess (1860–1927). When her period coincided with an epileptic attack, she took an ax to her parents and left them both bloody, both dead.

Lizzie had always been noted for "peculiar spells" that had all the symptoms of what is now called *epilepsy of the temporal lobe*, or *psychomotor epilepsy*. Popular opinion in

Fall River, Massachusetts, held that "poor Lizzie was always sort of crazy."

Her epileptic seizures came only during her menstrual period, and then only three or four times a year. The spells were brief, no more than an hour long, and ceased when Lizzie reached menopause. In the previous year, Lizzie had committed a daylight robbery of her own house during a menstrual-epileptic seizure. She had her period on August 4, 1892, the morning of the murders; this is a matter of court record.

Murder during an epileptic seizure is rare, and one cannot say that Lizzie killed her parents (actually, her father and stepmother) *because* of her epilepsy; but all evidence indicates that she killed the stepmother, at least, *during* a seizure. She had wanted to kill her stepmother earlier; the day before, she had tried to buy prussic acid (a form of cyanide) for the purpose, but the druggist refused to sell it to her. So she was forced to use an ax. Contrary to to folk rhyme, she gave her father only twenty whacks with the ax and her stepmother only ten.

At her inquest and trial, Lizzie benefited from the confusion of blood. Was the blood on her skirt menstrual or matricidal-patricidal? Menstruation was a delicate subject, especially when discussed in front of the all-male juries of that time. At the inquest, Lizzie was asked how a bloodstain could get on her skirt. She answered, "I have fleas" (still another euphemism for menstruation). The kind of spot she had could hardly be from her period, however. A female jury, Victoria Lincoln notes, would not have acquitted Lizzie, for women knew that

> over their heavy napkins, women wore ruffled drawers to the knee and short white petticoats under the underskirt. . . . A widish smear caused by a heavy period was quite possible; a small, clear-edged spot, so placed, would have been wildly improbable even if it had come from the inside, not the outside, of the garment.[7]

After she was acquitted of the murders—although everyone assumed she had committed them—Lizzie Borden was ostracized in Fall River, where she remained until her death. She is still, as far as we know, the only menstrual murderess.

· · · · · · · · · · · · · · · · ·

Chapter 24

MOVING THE MENSES, OR VICARIOUS MENSTRUATION

A woman does not have to bleed from the womb alone. The extremely rare phenomenon *vicarious menstruation* is a monthly bleeding from a mucous membrane other than the uterus. Most of the cases (70 percent) are *supplementary;* that is, bleeding occurs along with the regular menstrual flow. The other 30 percent are *substitutive;* that is, bleeding occurs some place other than the uterus, sometimes even after menopause.[1]

The most common place is the nose, the site of 30 percent of vicarious menstruation.[2] Most women's nasal mucosa become red and swollen before their periods. This swelling, aptly named *rhinorrhea,* is a part of the premenstrual syndrome. If unusual hormonal changes occur, the period may come in two places at once.[3]

Fortunately, the blood lost through vicarious menstruation is usually scanty. Vicarious menstruation has not been studied extensively. Physicians still cite a 1920 report by O. H. Roth, who examined 225 cases of vicarious menstruation reported between 1870 and 1920.[4] Roth found that 30 percent of the cases of bleeding occurred in the nose; 18 percent, in uterine ulcers; 8 percent each, in the skin and in the lungs; 5 percent, in the breasts; and the rest, in the stomach, mouth pharynx, bladder, ears, eyes, larynx, and vagina. (It should be recalled that the menstrual fluid, although it passes through the vagina, does not originate there. The uterus, not the vagina, bleeds.)

Vicarious menstruation does have its human-interest side. In 1882, J. T. Gordon reported the case of Mrs. H., who was forty-one years old and weighed 254 pounds. She had profuse bleeding from her thumb; the bleeding had occurred simultaneously with her period for more than three years. The bleeding lasted three to five days; a bandage around it had to be changed frequently. When the spot was not bleeding, it could be recognized "only by a slight blueness of the skin over an area not larger than a half pea." Mrs. H. reported no pain from her thumb while it was bleeding and added that "it rather feels good." [5]

It is tempting to regard the female *stigmatics*, those saints whose bodies bleed in different spots in imitation of Christ's wounds, as vicarious menstruators. However, the stigmata of three of the best known (Catherine de Ricci, Marie de Moerl, and Louise Lateau) appeared every Thursday noon through Friday afternoon, not monthly.

Why do the vicarious menstruate where they do? Psychoanalyst Helene Deutsch claims that the choice of organ for vicarious menstruation is determined by the patient's psyche.[6] There is little evidence to prove or disprove her, but there are medical reasons for the phenomenon.

Most common is sensitivity of some tissues to a high level of estrogen in the blood, with the mucous membranes of the nose being most likely to be affected by it. The other possible source of vicarious menstruation is surgical error. Bits of the lining of the womb may be mistakenly implanted in the incision during cesarean sections, removal of fibroid tumors, or in episiotomy during childbirth. The lining of the womb will menstruate wherever it is.

The unfortunate victims of medical mistakes or hormonal sensitivity can be helped. Vitamins K, C, and P will strengthen capillary walls. As the last resort, medical texts recommend "castration" (presumably hysterectomy). But for most women, who suffer nothing more serious than a nosebleed, vicarious menstruation is a minor annoyance.

Chapter 25

. . . .

ESCAPING THE MONTHLIES

"No woman would menstruate if she did not have to," Germaine Greer has said.[1] And it is a rare woman, indeed, who hasn't at some time wished she didn't menstruate; many a female has cursed the curse. But there is very little she can do about it except wait for pregnancy or menopause.

Medical texts list many causes for amenorrhea. Most are exotic, if not impossible to attain. Turner's syndrome, for instance, is characterized by a lack of periods. But women born with this syndrome also have low-set ears, a webbed neck, and a low intellect, and are unlikely to be more than 4 feet 8 inches in height. There is also the Stein-Leventhal syndrome, characterized by loss of menstruation and fertility, ovaries that are "oysterlike" in appearance, and abnormal growth of facial hair.

For those fortunate women who are neither dwarfs not bearded ladies, menstruation is virtually inescapable, although there have been attempts to thwart it. In 1934, a Los Angeles physician named George Starr White published a peculiar book entitled *The Emancipation of Women, or Regulating the Duration of the Menses*. White felt that women's periods are "unnatural," that the normal state is a natural mucous flow, like that of animals. Moreover, the more "naturally" a woman lived, the shorter the duration of her menses was, according to White.

Finally, he discovered a process called *Naturizing,* invented by his family physician to stop the menstrual flow for circus performers. It consists of the doctor's inserting a tampon under the uterus while pressing on a woman's abdomen. The next day, the doctor removes the tampon and replaces it. With this method, the flow usually does not last more than two or three days, regardless of previous bleeding. After four or five months, the average case becomes a "one-day woman"; after a year, she may be in the "one-hour class." [2]

White claims that the treatment was successful in fifteen case histories he provides and that it has added benefits. It eliminates pimples and rough skin, and the daughters and granddaughters and great-granddaughters of women treated this way have no blood in their menstrual flow, which lasts only a few hours.

The success of White's method seems unlikely; the inheritance of acquired characteristics, impossible. Nevertheless, White was attempting to fulfill a need that standard medical science has still not answered. What, indeed, does a circus performer do if she has a heavy flow?

There are several things she can do that will not work. In Katherine Anne Porter's *Old Mortality,* the girls suck on salt and lemon in order to stop their periods before going to a ball. Instead, they just make themselves sick. *Warren's Household Physician* (1901), a handbook commonly used around the turn of the century, strongly advises girls against dipping their feet in cold water to stop their periods. According to Warren, "The most lovely and innocent girls have done this for the purpose of attending a party; and, in some instances, the stoppage induced has ended in death within a few hours." [3]

In both of these instances, the girls want to halt their periods because of social events, not because their professional fulfillment might be impaired. Frivolous rather than serious reasons are given. Perhaps it is the same failure to take women seriously that has kept medicine from finding a way to end menstruation, short of menopause. Nevertheless, there are several ways, none of them conducive to good health, in which menstruation can be ended.

One is pathological dieting, the refusal to eat called *anorexia nervosa*, which is fundamentally an emotional disturbance. The woman with this disease is usually bright, articulate, self-disciplined, but with a horror of fat. She rarely eats more than token meals, may make herself vomit, and exercises compulsively. She will cease menstruating, but she may also starve to death if she is not given medical and psychological treatment.

Other illnesses may also cause missed periods. One is tuberculosis. White warns his readers against folklore: "The idea that the eradication of blood from the menstrual period will cause tuberculosis, is rank superstition and based on no finding of fact." [4] Instead, the reverse is true; tuberculosis in advanced stages will cause the eradication of the menses. But as in the case of anorexia nervosa, loss of periods is a sign of loss of good health.

Another illness that will end menstruation is heroin addiction. Addiction to opiates commonly causes infertility, lack of ovulation, and loss of menstruation, probably through the action of drugs on the hypothalamus, a part of the brain. In one study, 67 percent of women heroin addicts entering a methadone maintenance program menstruated infrequently, if at all. After they had been on methadone for two months, all but one resumed their regular periods. Poor nutrition is probably a factor in the missed periods (as it is with anorexia nervosa) because the women placed on methadone were also given better, supervised diets. Women addicts who withdraw without methadone take longer to regain their cycles.[5]

Menstruation can be eliminated through good health, claim the followers of Dr. Shelton's School of Hygiene. The Sheltonians see menstruation itself as the illness, as did the nineteenth-century gynecologist Dr. A. F. A. King. King's "cure" for the menstrual disease was continual pregnancies; Shelton's is proper care of the abdominal organs. As the common toad bloodlessly sheds its skin, as the bird bloodlessly sheds its feathers, so a *truly* healthy woman can shed her membranes without bleeding.[6] One woman has written to us that she has followed Shelton's prescription of diet and exercise and that she no longer menstruates.

Menstruation may also be ended by the atomic bomb. One of the effects of radiation sickness, as it appeared after the bombing of Hiroshima, was the cessation of menstruation. John Hersey writes in *Hiroshima:* "And, as if nature were protecting man against his own ingenuity, the reproductive processes were affected for a time; men became sterile, women had miscarriages, menstruation stopped." [7]

There remains the possibility of hysterectomy, the surgical method of ending menstruation. In a complete hysterectomy, the uterus is removed (the removal of the ovaries is called an *oophorectomy.*) With no uterus, there is no lining of the uterus; hence, no menstruation. Although many American doctors, as we have noted, are eager to perform hysterectomies (perhaps they should be called *remunerectomies*), the operation is a serious and expensive one and does not increase woman's control over her own body. She may also begin aging prematurely. It is not a practical solution to the bother of menstruation.

Undoubtedly the least unsafe suppressor of menstruation is the hormone. Hormones have been given to paraplegic and severely handicapped women and to women in plaster casts in order to stop their monthly bleeding until they are in better condition. The birth control pill and similar products can stop menstruation indefinitely if taken continually; prostitutes, as we have seen, use them for this purpose. But long-range side effects are unknown.

It is apparent that most "cures" for menstruation are worse than the curse. No one would prefer tuberculosis, heroin addiction, or the deadly embrace of an atomic bomb. But *menstrual extraction* may open a new era in women's history: an age of real control over our bodies, over the menstrual process.

Menstrual extraction was developed by women for women. A group of feminists in Los Angeles, at the Self-Help Clinic of the Feminist Women's Health Center, were troubled by menstruation and decided to end it. Lorraine Rothman, Carol Downer, and other women developed the technique, a very simple one.

In menstrual extraction, a woman or one of her friends may end her period almost as soon as it starts. When her bleeding begins, or when her period is due if she is late, she or her friend inserts into her uterus a tube (called a *cannula*) about one-tenth of an inch in diameter; this tube is attached to a collection bottle and to a syringe, about 6 inches long, that literally pumps out the period. The built-up lining of the womb, which is sloughed off naturally over several days of menstruation, is pumped away in minutes. Enthusiasts claim a "sixty-second period."

Menstrual extraction is not a backroom procedure. In November 1973, the feminists of Los Angeles presented a "Menstrual Extraction Review" for the American Public Health Association conference. The Self-Help Clinic performed a menstrual extraction for the women in the audience (the males, ten in an audience of over seventy people, were asked to leave and did so reluctantly.) The response from the women was wildly enthusiastic, and the historic event was recorded on video tape.[8]

Two of the most unusual practitioners of menstrual extraction are Lolly and Jeanne Hirsch, a mother-and-daughter team who also publish *The Monthly Extract: An Irregular Periodical*. Traveling mostly on the East Coast, they appear before women's groups, showing women how to examine their genitals and demonstrating menstrual extraction on each other.

For the Hirsches and for the rest of us, menstrual extraction is revolutionary. It is cheap, quick, simple. It eliminates belts, pads, pins, plugs, and pains except for possible cramping during extraction. It gives a woman complete control of her body, for if she is pregnant, the process serves as a *mini-abortion* (another term used for the procedure). And there's the rub—or one of them.

Today, menstrual extraction is embroiled in controversy. There are those who question its safety: Will it cause infection, which might lead to pain, fever, and possibly hospitalization and a D and C? It is true that the female organs are more prone to infection during menstruation than at any other time in a woman's cycle, but physicians disagree about the likelihood of uterine infections. Does menstrual extraction always work? No one can be certain.

There are legal questions: Is it abortion? If it is, the state and the medical profession would like to control it. Similarly, is it practicing medicine without a license? Again, the medical profession steps in.

Currently, there are no certain answers to these questions. The health establishment has involved itself directly in the process. Calling it *menstrual regulation,* doctors used it experimentally on the raped women of Bangladesh. Nor is the profit motive far behind. As early as 1971, Upjohn considered manufacturing a do-it-yourself extraction kit—in time for Christmas gift giving.

Menstrual extraction has become a political as well as a health issue. The safety factor is ignored when profit and population control are possible; men, especially one Harvey Karman of Los Angeles, have claimed that they invented the procedure and should control it. When Ellen Frankfort first described the extraction process in the *Village Voice* in 1971, she received dozens of letters of protest from doctors about its supposed dangers. But, says Frankfort, the doctors were

> more upset at the independence that period extraction in particular and self-help in general gave women rather than at the dangers of either. Few argued or even considered that the device could be made safer; none remembered that the first camera or radio or airplane was not perfect and that only in time could a new invention be judged.[9]

Menstrual extraction is by far the most exciting discovery of the women's health movement. At the same time, the extraction controversy bears watching because it illustrates contemporary menstrual politics at work; will we be able to keep our newfound control over our own bodies, or will we once again have to submit to men's definitions of our needs?

Part Seven

·   ·   ·   ·   ·   ·   ·   ·   ·   ·   ·   ·   ·   ·   ·   ·

MEN

Chapter 26

SAIGNADE: SIMULATED MENSTRUATION IN THE MALE

Not content to surround menstruation with images of filth and fear, man has tried for at least a few aeons to learn how to do it himself. From time to time, men have participated either physically or intellectually in the *couvade,* the imagined motherhood of the male (from *couver,* "to hatch"). In certain societies, men imitate their wives as they give birth, suffer the pains, and receive all the attention when it's over.

Analogies to couvade abound in Western literature and myth. In Hemingway's story "Indian Camp," the Indian husband is so upset by his wife's pain in giving birth that he slits his own throat. In the medieval French romance, *Aucassin et Nicolette,* Aucassin gives birth, but he is beaten for so doing. Even some of the Greek gods are born without mothers: Athena from Zeus's forehead; Dionysus from his thigh; Aphrodite from Cronus's testicles thrown into the sea. All these seem to represent a male refusal to allow the birth-giving function to be solely female; the men want to share in and to define the act themselves.

Mary Ellmann points out the subtle couvade in Malamud's *The Fixer:*

The heroism is that of a spiritual pregnancy. Yakov Bok, we are steadily told, does not seek out or demand his ordeal, he receives it. . . . The virtues of Bok are those of the pregnant woman: endurance, patience, the gradual growth and focusing of purpose. The end of the book is the incipient delivery: Bok is on his way to some kind of birth.[1]

The Fixer also contains, in effect, the imagined menstruation of the male. There is no term for that. Perhaps *saignade* would be analogous to couvade (from *saigner,* "to bleed").

Many primitive societies impose on their young men a puberty rite that causes them to bleed from the genitals. The boys are therefore able to mark their initiation into adulthood with a dramatic physical sign that can be equated with the menarche of the girls. More advanced civilizations have abandoned such rites, but they incorporate in their literature allusions to the male's desire to imitate, control, or assimilate the female functions within his own body, to compensate for the lack of a womb and a vagina.

Classic interpretations of male puberty rites such as *circumcision* (the cutting of the foreskin from the penis) and *subincision* (slitting the underside of the penis along the urethra, producing a permanent disfigurement of the form and function of the penis) do not include envy. They rely on the psychoanalytic interpretation that circumcision is a symbolic castration of sons by fathers and on the anthropological view that circumcision was a rite of initiation into adult society. Read, the first anthropologist to study these rites in depth, went a little farther. He believed that the male mutilations expressed a rigid sexual solidarity among the men and the essential opposition of the community of male interests to the "sphere of women." [2] Read's views satisfied most students of this field until some began to probe more deeply into the causes of this supposed antagonism between men and women.

Bruno Bettelheim, in 1954, was the first to look beyond castration anxiety and male superiority as causes of the bloody initiation rites and to offer instead "the premise that one sex feels envy in regard to the sexual organs and functions of the other." [3] He was not talking about penis envy, which originates, according to Freud, when a little girl, seeing a boy's penis for the first time, immediately assumes that it must be better for masturbation than her own minuscule clitoris and wants one for herself. Her quest for a penis will never be completely satisfied, but she will find contentment if she will accept her mother role and the child in the womb as the next-best thing to a penis. There are today many reasons to question this theory, especially in the light of long-established anthropological evidence of couvade. But Freud's work is so important to the understanding of the human psyche that even his most tenuous theories have been swept along to respectability in the tidal wave of his influence. Bettelheim's premise, on the other hand, is that men envy women their ability to bear children. Joseph Campbell, the mythologist explains:

> The fear of woman and the mystery of her motherhood have been for the male no less impressive imprinting forces than the fears and mysteries of the world of nature itself. And there may be found in the mythologies and ritual traditions of our entire species innumerable instances of the unrelenting efforts of the male to relate himself effectively—in the way, so to say, of an antagonistic cooperation—to these two alien yet intimately constraining forces: woman and the world.[4]

By "the world," Campbell means such things as the change of seasons, the rhythms of the moon and the tides, processes that even the most primitive human link in the great chain of being could recognize as being analogous to the lives of women: the twenty-eight-day lunar cycle, on which he believed the menstrual cycle was dependent; the growth, ripening, and fall of fruit from the trees, so like the bursting fecundity of women. To maintain a dominance over mysterious, bleeding woman, man had to assimilate woman's functions within himself: to bleed from the genitals, to give birth, and to assume a ritual maternity in order to fool the goddesses of nature into accepting him as the dominant sex.

The most widespread male puberty rite among all the preliterate peoples of the earth is circumcision. So important is the cutting of the foreskin that it is still widely practiced today on infant boys as a hygiene measure. Elizabeth Gould Davis theorizes that the practice originated in the mythical days when a "mountain of foreskins" was showered on the

Great Goddess in tribute and at the insistence of the ruling women.[5] Yet, women were not even mentioned when circumcision became the sign of the covenant between the Hebrew patriarchal God and his chosen people.

Bettelheim, by linking circumcision rites with ancient fertility rites, rather than with simple rites of passage, advances the convincing hypothesis that genital mutilation is a direct attempt by the male to overcome the problem of woman's ascendancy in procreation. He stresses the importance in primitive societies of bestowing the severed foreskin on one's mother, sister, or another female who will then wear it, honor it, cook it, and eat it. In return, the male expects to receive symbolically that female's power of maternity. For example, certain rituals of circumcision emphasize that by shedding genital blood the boy will assume the powers of menstruation and childbearing possessed by the mythical women of the Creation stories. In Australian myth, circumcision is said to originate with a semihuman bird, *Jurijurilja;* the bird throws a boomerang that, on its return, circumcises the bird and cuts the vulvas of its wives, causing the first menstruation.

The extreme secrecy of boys' puberty rites, Bettelheim believes, is closer than any other tribal phenomenon to the secrecy among the women surrounding the act of childbirth. He suggests that the men exclude women from any knowledge of their secret rites in retaliation for woman's refusal to share the mysteries of childbirth. Men of one Australian tribe go to such lengths to enforce a ritual solidarity that they attempt to convince their women that they do not defecate. Boys' rectums are stopped up temporarily as part of the puberty rite, but the women are led to believe that the blockage is permanent. If a man becomes incapacitated through illness, his wife is told by the others that the illness is responsible for the rupture of the seal of puberty. The image of men constantly hiding their feces from the women suggests vividly the image of women hiding their menstrual rags from the eyes of men, both believing they are preserving the integrity of their own sex and its secrets.

We give prolonged attention to Bettelheim's theories here because they seem in accord with the belief that fear of woman's procreative powers is one of the most profound of human imprints. Although classic anthropological explanations for the origin of circumcision claim that it is a hygienic practice, a preparation for sex life, a test of endurance, a tribal mark, a sacrifice to the goddess of fertility, or a sanctification of the generative faculties, such explanations tend to overlook that in causing himself to bleed from his genitals, man is *pretending to menstruate.* He is thereby recreating in himself the role that biology has assigned exclusively to women. *What actually happens* at adolescent circumcision is at least as important as the ceremony's sociological implications.

The rites of subincision, practiced almost exclusively in Australia, intensify this belief. It follows circumcision in the sequence of the initiation rites. Unlike circumcision, which can occur only once, subincision frequently takes place two or three times, as a further assimilation of female power in the maturing male. In an extreme case, the tribesmen of the Wogeo Islands of New Guinea periodically incise the penis and allow blood to flow to rid themselves of the impurities of sexual intercourse, of which women are naturally cleansed by menstruation.[6]

Ashley Montagu is one who believes that subincision is simulated menstruation, based on the bloodletting common to both and the "feminization" of the appearance of the penis that results.[7] Men who have been subincised are forced to urinate in a squatting position, like women. Even more convincingly, Gésa Róheim notes that the subincised penis is called *vagina* in the sacred songs; blood squirting from the penis is described by words that mean "women" or "milk." And during the ritual in one tribe, the subject runs backward in a creek, flicking up his penis to show the wound; the words for vagina and creek are used interchangeably.[8] Some tribes use parallel names for menstrual blood and blood from the subincision wound.

More evidence of the womb envy in boys' initiation rites is revealed when boys' rites are compared with girls'. A girl's initiation normally follows the first appearance of her menstrual blood. The flowing of the blood is the significant event; what happens at the rites merely commemorates nature's decision. The timing of the first menstruation is beyond the control of the girls or their elders; the aerial spirits or supernatural snakes that bring on the menarche do not invade several pubescent vaginas at once. Consequently, most of the societies studied tend to conduct separate initiation rites for each girl who reaches her menarche (although in some places girls who have already been initiated may take part in a new girl's ceremony).

Because there is no spontaneous biological event that heralds adulthood in a boy, boys of an appropriate age are usually initiated in groups. In these group rites, the all-important fertility aspect of the ceremony gets submerged in the appearances of induction into the tribe. Perhaps this is one reason why the imitative character of such rites has so long been overlooked; it has been too easy to make the obvious connection between puberty rites in primitive societies and the initiation rites of fraternal organizations of all types, which have been popular for centuries throughout the Western world. Yet, even in those fraternal rites, there must be a suggestion of men imitating women, of men getting together to share trivial or ritual secrets with one another because they are perpetually excluded from the greatest secret of all.

A dramatic example of the male attempt to control menstruation by assimilating it to himself is given by the French historian Jules Michelet (1798–1874). He avidly recorded the details of the menstruation of his young wife, Athénaïs Mialaret, whom he married when he was fifty-one and she was twenty-three.

Michelet was fascinated with blood and with woman. He defines historical characters by the quality of their blood: for example, the thin blood of Robespierre is opposed to the carmine and generous blood of the people. Woman is the incarnation of nature; like nature, she is ruled by rhythms. Woman represents grace and emotion; man, law and intellect. Michelet is interested in woman as spectacle, in watching, not to possess her, but to uncover her.

Hence, although Michelet reports that his wife was frigid and rarely allowed sexual consummation, he adored watching her, especially when she was menstruating. He studied her intestinal life in order to shed light on the vaginal. Apparently, she complied with his study, even with his whims; on one occasion, he sat below her while she added a few drops to the sea.

Michelet wanted to serve as his wife's *"homme femme-de-chambre,"* serving all the functions of a maid and friend. He had much opportunity, for she was frequently ill. He wanted to be her mentor; supervising her studies of insects, he taught her also to watch. He liked to think of the sexes being assimilated to one another. He wrote a fantasy about a couple who constantly impregnated each other; he said his wife impregnated him with her perfume.

Beginning in 1857 and lasting through 1860, Michelet's *Journal* contains much about sex and especially about menstruation. From Michelet, one can chart his wife's menstrual cycles. In 1857, *les règles* arrived June 30, then July 30; he remarks that the second period was five days late. As in this case, he usually anticipates a twenty-five-day cycle, although his wife's ranges from twenty-five to thirty days. He becomes upset at deviations from the cycle, but sometimes, he makes obvious counting mistakes. Usually, he also gives the time of day that her period arrived; sometimes, he describes the color.

He does not, however, criticize superstitions surrounding her periods. Apparently, she was not to bathe during them, for he says at one point that she took a bath too soon afterward. He sees nothing odd in her washing her own chemise so that the laundress will not know of her menstruation, although it sounds to a modern reader like an avoidance of taboo. Probably, some superstition is behind his surprise that she has a bloody nose during her period.[9]

Why is Michelet so fascinated by menstruation? As a historian, Michelet wants to record and, by recording, have a sense of mastery. He wants to subsume his wife in himself, assimilating both male and female. Menstruation in Michelet's journals can be read as a symbol of his desire to consume woman, especially those of her processes most closely connected with the rhythms of nature. In this, he is clearly not alone.

Chapter 27

. . . .

CYCLES AND RHYTHM IN MEN

When Shakespeare has his Julius Caesar proclaim, "I am constant as the northern star," the Bard may have been making use of the usual stereotypes: women are flighty, men firm; females are emotional, males are reasonable; women have cycles, men don't.[1] Julius Caesar (or Shakespeare) was wrong. Although most men do not bleed from their genitals every month as women do, men's behavior does follow distinct cycles. Even epilepsy (Julius Caesar's "falling sickness") may be cyclical. And unlike women's periodic bleedings, "raging hormonal imbalances" in men may be all the more dangerous because they are less predictable.

Both sexes are subject to *circadian,* or twenty-four-hour, cycles: a flux in hormones, moods, strengths, and weaknesses. Those lucky persons whose body times are synchronized with their work hours will find that their temperatures rise in the morning, giving them a greater push to get up and go; their temperatures will drop in the evening. Circadian rhythms are difficult to alter: night-shift workers are more likely to have nervous disorders or ulcers. The phenomenon of jet lag, which strikes the traveler who flies overnight to Peking or Vietnam, is widespread; often mental efficiency will be affected by it.

Most males are conditioned to see themselves as overcoming such rhythms, such external forces: their "manhood" may be dependent on such a self-image. But a chink in the armor appeared in the 1974 perjury case of California Lieutenant Governor Ed Reinecke. One of Reinecke's defenses was that because of jet lag after a trip from California to Washington, D.C., he may not have known what he was saying.

Monthly rhythms are, perhaps inevitably, more difficult for men to face because we are all taught that only females suffer from periodic craziness. But as early as 1897, it was noted that both sexes bleed periodically with lung hemorrhages, hemorrhoids, and hyperemia of the liver. A research study in 1933 observed monthly epilepsy attacks in the "stronger sex." [2]

The male menstrual (the word means "monthly") cycle does not confine itself to diseases. Dr. Rex Hersey of the University of Pennsylvania studied factory workers in 1929 and 1930. He chose to observe "average" and "well-adjusted" workers and managers, those who seemed "normal" in overt respects.[3] For a year, he interviewed each man four times a day, made regular physical examinations, and interviewed the men's families. He arrived, finally, at charts for each individual, showing that emotional variations were predictable not only in twenty-four hour (circadian) cycles but also in a near-monthly rhythm, a cycle of four to six weeks.

One twenty-two-year-old man showed a four-and-a-half week cycle, with variations no greater than those in a woman's menstrual cycle. During low periods, he was apathetic at home and at work; he temporarily abandoned his artwork. Another man with a five- to six-week cycle had manic periods during which he felt outgoing and confident, with great vigor and energy. During his low periods, he found work a burden, needed more sleep, and preferred to sit quietly. In his manic periods, he slept less and even weighed less.

One happy sixty-year-old in the study claimed that he never changed (the "I am as constant as the northern star" syndrome). He, it turned out, had a nine-week cycle. His mood decline was so gradual that he did not realize he was criticizing his superiors, refusing to make jokes with his colleagues, and in general, withdrawing. Yet, if he had accepted (as women must because of their bleeding) the role of cycles in his life, he would have had a much better understanding of himself.

"Flighty women" are usually the butts of jokes about "women drivers." But men drivers, it has been shown, have higher accident rates. Even the Auto Safety Committee of the conservative American Medical Association concluded that women are better drivers because "they're less emotional than men."

Men drivers do, indeed, have their ups and downs, monthly ones. Estelle Ramey relates this incident in her *Ms.* article on men's cycles: The Omi Railway Company of Japan directs a private transportation system in Kyoto and Osaka, operating more than 700 buses and taxis in dense traffic areas. The directors of the company became concerned in 1969 over the high losses resulting from accidents. The company's efficiency experts began a study of each man working for the company, trying to discover his lunar cycle of mood and efficiency. Then, they adjusted schedules and routes to coincide with the best time of the month for each worker. Since then, traffic has increased, but the Omi accident rate has dropped an amazing one-third.

If monthly cycles in normal men can be damaging, what of the abnormal? Adolescent boys have been known to have monthly psychotic episodes, which may be the male equivalent of premenstrual tension. Monthly oscillations are common in manic-depressive psychosis, catatonic fits, epilepsy, and its close cousin, migraine.

Periodic illnesses may be the effects of sudden excitement in certain regions of the brain, especially the hypothalamus (which regulates many basic body functions, such as temperature). Periodic illnesses may come from changes in the number of certain blood cells or from local swelling of tissues and skin, concurrent fever, and edema (an abnormal accumulation of fluid, also characteristic of the premenstrual syndrome in women). Periodic edema may be inherited through a dominant gene.

One's ethnic group may determine one's periodic illness. Peritonitis (inflammation of the membrane that lines the abdomen) is periodic mainly within Mediterranean ethnic groups:

Jews, Armenians, Arabs. Periodic edema, however, appears to be limited to Northern European types, limited, that is, to most of the men who run things in the United States and who try to keep our ship of state on an even keel.[4]

When Dr. Edgar Berman said that women are unfit for leadership because of "raging hormonal imbalances," he neglected the role hormones play in men. In Denmark, for instance, a sixteen-year study charted the fluctuating amounts of male sex hormones in men's urine.[5] The discovery: the ebb and flow of hormones followed a pronounced thirty-day rhythm. The male hormonal balance was constantly changing.

In *The Menstrual Cycle*, Katharina Dalton argues that there is no evidence for male cycles because no cyclical patterns have been found in such aspects as school infractions, eye pain in glaucoma, blood pressure, and lower pain threshhold. But Dalton inadvertently describes another form of men's cycles, one that we might call, for lack of any other name, the *vicarious cycle*.[6]

Just as males sometimes feel sympathetic labor pains (couvade) when their wives are giving birth, men also show symptoms when the women around them menstruate. In one case, a salesman's selling ability changed mysteriously for one week in every four. For three weeks he averaged $200 a week in commissions; every fourth week, his earnings fell to around $50. During the weeks his earnings were low, he became more depressed and started to work later. When he checked his wife's menstrual record, he found that his "low week" coincided with her premenstrual symptoms: irritability and fatigue.

Another man had chronic bronchitis, with periodic intensifications correlating with his wife's periods. After she had an ovarian cyst removed, his periodic attacks disappeared. In a British study of industrial workers, some men had monthly spells of lateness. These, it turned out, occurred when the wife or mother had overslept or was slower than usual preparing sandwiches or breakfast because of her menstrual cycles. In these instances, the sharing of household duties clearly would have benefited both sexes.[7]

Even children may react vicariously to their mother's periods. Dalton, studying children brought to a doctor's office with colds, found that 50 percent were brought by the mother while she was in the four days before or during menstruation. In one case, three-year-old Keith had colds every month, coinciding with his mother's menstruations. Dalton, in effect, sees the mother as the cause of the child's illess. It is possible, however, that mothers at "that time of the month" are simply more concerned about their offspring's well-being, more likely to fuss over them, more likely to take them to the doctor.[8]

It is undeniable that there are male cycles. Scientific evidence points to biological, circadian, monthly, and emotional rhythms. But there is also an imaginative and appealing cyclic theory that has had its own ups and downs in popularity over the years.

Occasionally, newspapers and magazines carry ads about *biorhythms*, claiming that the formula to be sold will teach the reader to chart his own cycle and plan his activities to his advantage. These formulas go back to the eccentric Wilhelm Fliess, who in 1887 published *The Rhythm of Life: Foundations of an Exact Biology.*[9]

According to Fliess, everyone is bisexual. The "male component" of this bisexuality (consisting of such traditionally male qualities as strength, endurance, and courage) is keyed to a cycle of twenty-three days. The "female component" (not menstrual bleeding, but a cycle of sensitivity, intuition, love, and other feelings) has a period of twenty-eight days. Fliess believed that both cycles are present in every cell and counter each other throughout life. Moreover, they are shown in the ups and downs of each person's physical and mental vitality. And, finally, they may be used eventually to determine the date of one's death. In the 1930s, a teacher at Innsbruck added a third dimension to Fliess's theory: a thirty-three-day creativity cycle of mental acuteness and power.

Fliess's rather bizarre theory would have been forgotten except for Freud, who was a friend and a passionate devotee of Fliess. Fliess linked his twenty-three- and twenty-eight-day cycles with the changes in the mucosal lining of the nose. He spoke of the "genital cells" in the interior of the nose and related nasal irritation to neurotic symptoms and sexual abnormalities. His treatment: diagnosing ills by inspecting the nose and applying cocaine to its interior. Fliess even operated twice on Freud's nose.

The main objection to Fliess's theories is this: There is no proof that they correspond with reality in any way. Like remarks about hormonal imbalances, they may represent a wish fulfillment, a desire to create order through pigeonholing men and women into biological models.

Although Dr. Berman envisioned hazardous possibilities if "a menopausal President" had presided over the Cuban missile crisis in 1962, many American presidents have survived hormonal and/or cyclical disabilities. Thomas Jefferson had periodic migraines; Abraham Lincoln had periodic depressions. At least one writer suggested that Richard Nixon's "raging hormonal imbalances" may have caused the Watergate morass. Even John F. Kennedy, who did preside over the Cuban missile crisis, had a serious hormonal disorder, Addison's disease (adrenal insufficiency). Moreover, a man old enough to be eligible for the presidency is liable to be in worse physical health than his female counterpart. Not only does she live longer, but her menopause is likely to be more manageable than his, if only because it has been more fully observed and understood.

More has been written about the male menopause than about any other aspect of the male cycle. For women, their menopause is more immediately obvious: an end to monthly bleeding. Psychologically, of course, it is complicated by other factors: society's devaluing older women, in part because they are no longer youthfully beautiful; the woman's losing her children to adulthood.

For a man, the *menopause* or *male climacteric* (the words are used interchangeably) is more insidious. The men are likely to be at the height of their careers, but at the same time, there is a decrease, usually gradual, in the secretion of testosterone, the male hormone. There are also the usual fears of death and aging.

What are the symptoms of the male menopause? Loss of sexual potential is one, almost certainly traceable to the decline in testosterone production. By the time a man reaches age sixty-five, he may require medical assistance to continue a full sex life. Not only does the menopausal male lose sexual potency, but he is also characterized by indecisiveness, irritability, vasomotor troubles (the contraction and dilation of blood vessels), general ineptness, insecurity, and uncertainty. The sexual changes of the male climacteric are perhaps the most worrisome to him because they most closely involve his "manhood."

In our years in colleges and universities, we have observed a particular syndrome that seems characteristic of the male menopause in academia. At about the time a man becomes a full professor with tenure (in his early or middle forties, say), he usually begins attending academic conventions more frequently and without his wife. At the conventions, he seeks out young women to tell them "My wife doesn't understand me"; or if he's trying to be more hip, he explains about his "open marriage." He mentions that he's in a position to hire new faculty and that he wants to interview the young woman for the job—in his room or for lunch or for dinner, but at some point, in his room.

When he returns home, he often becomes the mentor of his female students, who are flattered by his attention. He may seek out new young women each semester, or he may shed his old wife for a new one, marrying a student twenty years his junior. For a while at least, he has come to terms with his own aging. Not seeing across from him the woman who aged along with him, he is not reminded of his own bodily changes. At the height of his career, his increase in power serves as a partial substitute for a decrease in potency. Hence, the male academic successfully weathers his crisis.

Successful men in all professions have played this familiar role for themselves and the women in their lives. We don't know what happens to those less successful ones who have to suffer the same physical diminutions without the protecting emoluments of money and status—or what happens to the women they leave behind. Perhaps because men, who run the scientific establishment, would prefer to deny the existence of male cycles, there has been little research done on the subject. Men, because of their socially conditioned role, find it more comfortable to believe they are as constant as the northern star. But it would benefit us all to know more about the forces controlling us. As the old saw goes, time and tide wait for no man; but if we understand the time and the tide, perhaps we can be waiting for them.

CONCLUSION:
LIFTING THE CURSE

The long silence has been broken. Menstruation is ceasing to be a subject for whispered confidences, muttered during the seclusion of slumber parties and coffee klatches. Not only are women beginning to talk to each other frankly and casually about their common bond; contemporary feminist artists are forcing us literally to look at our bleedings. Today, menstruation appears as theme or subject in the graphic arts, in painting and sculpture, in feminist comic strips, and in menstrual shows of all kinds.

Despite the menstrual taboos of the primitives, visual representations of the period are actually very old. Menstruation, pregnancy, and birth appear in prehistoric rock drawings of North America,[1] and there is some evidence that ancient peoples may have used the menstrual cycle for telling time. According to Bart Jordan, a contemporary anthropologist, various "menstrual notations" helped the ancients keep track of weeks and months. The notations include arrow strokes, rosettes, and square-framed symbols. Examples of these notations have been found in the Old World and, from eras thousands of years later, in native American sites.[2]

The menstrual notation symbol frequently used to denote two fortnights bears some resemblance to two frogs sitting back to back with a moon between them. The frogs have what Jordan calls "womb-like body lines." Out of this figure, according to Jordan, developed the prototypical female fertility figure: the steatopygous Venus, with her exaggerated breasts, hips, and thighs. Jordan sees this new design as evidence of the sophistication of ancient artists and mathematicians; for us, it is a sign of the hold menstruation had on the primitive mind. It was not enough to record menstrual data, as if recording meant control of the mysterious process; the period also had to be domesticated into art, the menstrual symbol transformed into woman in her most acceptable role.

At least one modern artist has tried to return to folklore and found menstruation. Faith Wilding, who has exhibited her work in California, was raised in Paraguay and became interested in what she calls "female mythology," especially its "very primitive sources." [3] Her constructions use such symbols as eggs, rocks, shells, and blood; some use the form of the Venus of Willendorf, the best-known steatopygous Venus. Wilding particularly uses the triangle as a symbol of the vagina.

She rejects the idea of female "mystery," but instead tries to make "the blood rituals of women" (menstruation, pregnancy and birth, lactation, and menopause) into rites invested with magic. As feminist art historian Arlene Raven suggests, Wilding is concerned with "transubstantiation—to the body and blood of the spirit." In one Wilding construction, grass skirts cover but do not conceal a triangular form, open in the center, with a suggestion of blood hanging from it.

Wilding's forms are a return to the past, perhaps to an Amazon nation. But it is Judy Chicago, also a Californian, who is most responsible for the breaking of the menstrual taboo in modern art. No folklore could be as striking as Chicago's handmade lithograph *Red Flag* (1971). Chicago's intent was frankly political. She wrote us:

> I wanted to validate overt female subject matter in the art community and chose to do so by making "Red Flag" as a handmade litho, which is a high art process, usually confined to much

more neutralized subject matter. By using such overt content in this form, I was attempting to introduce a new level of permission for women artists. It really worked.

Red Flag is at first shocking, a red flag designed to enrage puritanical souls. The picture, in tones of pink and gray and black, shows one nude female leg, softly shadowed. The other leg is obscured by a hand that is removing a reddened tampon by pulling on the string. Although the average woman may perform this ritual thousands of times in her lifetime, she probably has never seen it pictured. She probably has never watched another woman remove a tampon. Thus does an act most of us would class simply as personal acquire the dimensions of a taboo.

Judy Chicago's later theories have become a focus for much controversy, centering on her insistence that round, pulsating womblike forms (such as the froglike figures Bart Jordan discovered) are an intrinsically female imagery. What is undeniable is that Chicago has made an enormous contribution to freeing women artists from the menstrual taboo, not only in *Red Flag* but in her classes at Fresno State, the California Institute of the Arts, and the Feminist Studio Workshop, in which she encourages students to express their feelings about womanhood through art.

At Cal Arts, she, Faith Wilding, and about twenty other women artists constructed *Womanhouse*. Convincing an elderly woman to donate an old, ramshackle house to them, they transformed it into a grand symbol of female culture. In the kitchen, there are aprons in the shape of breasts and lips; fried eggs are transformed to breasts. In the nursery, there are androgynous toys, built larger than usual to give adults the feeling of smallness children have. In the closet, there are hundreds of shoes, including spike heels decorated with real spikes. In one bedroom, a woman sits, endlessly applying makeup to her face.

Another bathroom became Judy Chicago's *Menstruation Bathroom*. The room is covered with a gauze veil and is white, clean, and deodorized. On a shelf are Modess and Tampax boxes; the wastebasket overflows with used napkins. On the floor, a saturated tampon lurks. Judy Chicago has written,

"However we feel about our own menstruation is how we feel about seeing its image in front of us."

Chicago reports to us that men are especially fascinated with *Menstruation Bathroom.* She ties their interest to what happens to boys in adolescence: They identify with their mothers but

> are forced by social pressure, to make an identification with men. . . . This is symbolized for many men by that moment in school when the girls are taken into the other room and shown a film on menstruation—the secret, so to speak, puberty ritual that separated the boys from the girls. Seeing the bathroom was a connection to the mother, to the female, to that which has been forbidden to them.

Although Chicago is interested in men's responses to her *Menstruation Bathroom,* she and other contemporary feminist artists are more concerned with liberating women's creative potential from the cultural censorships imposed on purely female experiences. Judith Jurasek, for example, titles her sculptural weaving *The Subject Is Taboo.* Her piece, which hangs from the ceiling, is large and in the colors of menstrual fluid: bright blood red to black and dark maroon. A furry covering sits over dark blood-red pods or drops of stuffed vinyl, along with long black and red yarn fringes. The overall shape is a modified mound, narrow at the top, wide at the base. It symbolizes both the placenta of birth and the blood of menstruation, two aspects of uniquely female life. Its womblike form is the kind of female imagery Judy Chicago discusses.

Mary Beth Edelson's *Blood Mysteries* invites women to participate in the artwork. The figure of a powerfully built nude woman, with a circle around her abdomen and flowing hair surrounding her head, is drawn on a wall above a real wooden box that is divided into four compartments: Menstruation Stories, Blood Power Stories, Menopause Stories, and Birth Stories. Women viewing the piece were asked to contribute their experiences on the topics and place their stories in the box. Women generally expressed pleasure with the chance to share their experiences; much hostility came from men.

One of the Blood Power Stories contributed is about the

takeovers of the Whitney Museum in New York by women artists. The protestors had been objecting to the Whitney's evident sexism in giving scant attention to the work of women artists, and protests have been annual events since 1970. What is rarely mentioned in media reports is the women's symbolic actions: strewing raw eggs around the galleries and festooning the Whitney with tampons.

But the center for menstrual shows in America is hardly New York; it is California, especially the Los Angeles area. Isabel Welsh, a political science student at the University of California, has created a traveling theater piece, *Menstrual Blood;* two writer-artists in Laguna Beach have produced the hilariously raunchy *Tits & Clits;* Womanspace, a gallery and all-around meeting center for L.A. women, has sponsored "Menstruation Weekends."

Welsh's menstrual show (the first event of the "Menstruation Weekend") is a thirty-minute tape collage of women talking about their menstruation experiences, mixed with readings on the subject from Doris Lessing, Mary McCarthy, and Colette and short quotations about menstrual pollution in so-called primitive societies. Simultaneously, technicolor slides are flashed on three screens of Welsh using Kotex, Tampax, Tassaway,

> spray deodorants, douches, etc.—lots of blood—and very graphic—the piece is broken in the middle with a woman in a white jacket who reads a brief, dry medical statement on the physiology of menstruation. After the tape and slides are finished, there is a "ritual" ending, the symbolic tasting of menstrual blood.

Welsh sees her piece as presenting a "positive ritual" for a "confused secular society." She uses her material to help others get at their true feelings about "body images"; like Chicago, Edelson, and the other feminist artists, she seeks to have all women liberated from menstrual taboos.

Less serious than Welsh but perhaps in its way more striking is "The Menses Is the Message!", one of the stories in *Tits & Clits*, an adult comic book.[4] Mary Multipary, the heroine of the story, feels a general depression, then realizes it's "merely premenstrual tension." Because all is explained, she feels cheerful again. Mary then suffers through all the tabooed torments we've been exploring in this book. There are no directions on how to insert two tampons at one time; the tampons leak too easily and must be changed constantly, especially with an IUD; carnivorous hemophile dogs chase bloody Mary down the street.

Finding herself broke and still menstruating, Mary tries to wash her used sanitary napkins in the laundry. Unfortunately, she becomes absorbed in a Wonder Woman comic—pondering the question, "Does Wonder Woman work during her period?"—and her napkins disintegrate in the washer.

But then lucky Mary finds a "Berkeley book by Alicia Grapevine, a sister" (obviously a reference to Alicia Bay Laurel's *Living on the Earth*), that tells her to cut a rubber sponge to size. Mary carves her sponge into a phallus and exults in how good it feels. She decides to wear it all the time for "that nice feeling of being loved." Delighted with her discovery, Mary decides to have a party for her women friends, and they all cut sponges for menstrual use. Mary says, "The men would say we're having a 'poke-her' game"; Mary's friend is more outspoken when she tries on the sponge: "The hell with the old man! This is fun!" In the final panels, Mary and her friends do a sisterly cheer and dance: "No more cotton! No more hooks! No more boxboy's knowing looks!"

Tits & Clits may provoke outrage or applause, but like Judy Chicago's *Red Flag* and Isabel Welsh's ritual blood tasting, it is a great breakthrough toward ending menstrual taboos. Furthermore, its jaunty drawing style and dialogue suggest possibilities for releasing more and more of the embarrassed laughter that fills the air when women furtively share their common experiences.

When we became involved with this book, we felt—like Judy Chicago, like Isabel Welsh, like all the feminist artists—that we needed a ritual of female culture to inspire us. There were no precedents, so we created our own: a "Bleed-In."

We chose Friday, July 13, 1973, for our "Bleed-In" because Friday, the number thirteen, and the full moon (it shone on us that night) are all ancient female symbols. By chance, thirteen women attended the party, held at Mary Jane's house in Baltimore.

For the occasion, Mary Jane had decorated the bathroom with the signs and symbols of menstruation. Large paper flowers were hanging from the mirror and the door. Stained pads (tomato sauce) were lying at random on the floor. Near the red wastebasket lay a pair of white pants with a red "Friday" stitched on the front and a telltale stain on the crotch, meant to recall the high school myth that a girl who wore red on Friday "had the rag on." Red yarn dangled from the rim of the toilet, and Erica Jong's poem "Gardener" was pasted on the door. On the wall was a piece of paper, titled "Menstrual Graffiti," on which women wrote such witticisms as "We all need someone we can bleed on"; "Woman's place is in the bathroom"; and "Vampire to schoolteacher: See you next period."

In the living room, we all sat in a circle (a female, womb-like form). By chance, the two women who were menstruating were sitting a half-circle apart, so everyone was encircled by them. We told anecdotes of our first periods and discovered three of us were wearing white when "it came"; two were at camp. All had feelings of helplessness and embarrassment; some had never shared those experiences before, despite years of consciousness-raising groups. We toasted our stories with the drink of the evening: a Bloody Mary.

Later in the evening, we viewed the educational films from Modess and Kotex and the video tape of eight older women discussing menopause. Watching the movies together removed the last traces of self-consciousness by giving an ordinary focus to this extraordinary event. By the end of the evening, it became clear—to the three of us, especially—that our "Bleed-In" had given a new meaning to our idea of sisterhood. We had brought together in the city of Baltimore thirteen American women to share menstrual experiences and gain self-awareness. But we had also brought those thirteen women together with their sisters in ancient Cambodia, prehistoric New Guinea, contemporary Israel. Beneath the hilarity and irreverence of the evening was a solemn celebration of women's mysteries, an attempt to honor what is generally defiled, to raise to consciousness what has been repressed in fear for millennia. That we had so much fun at our rites is a positive sign that we succeeded. We believe that this generation of women will ultimately exorcise the curse over us all as we pass "Eve's blessing" on to our daughters.

NOTES

CHAPTER 1. WOMEN IN THE CLOSET: TABOOS OF EXCLUSION

1. Franz Steiner, *Taboo* (Baltimore: Penguin, 1956), p. 21.

2. Sigmund Freud, *Totem and Taboo* (New York: Dodd, Mead, 1919), p. 128.

3. M. J. Meggitt, "Male-Female Relationships in the Highlands of Australian New Guinea," *American Anthropologist* 66 (1964).

4. Theodor Reik, *Pagan Rites in Judaism* (New York: Farrar, Straus, 1964), pp. 87–88.

5. George D. Thomson, *Studies in Ancient Greek Society* (London: Lawrence, 1949), p. 205.

6. Mary Chadwick, *The Psychological Effects of Menstruation* (New York: Nervous & Mental Disease, 1932), p. 6.

7. Bruno Bettelheim, *Symbolic Wounds: Puberty Rites and the Envious Male* (New York: Collier, 1962), p. 137.

8. Elizabeth Davis, *The First Sex* (Baltimore: Penguin, 1972), p. 92.

9. William N. Stephens, *A Cross-cultural Study of Menstrual Taboos* (Provincetown, Mass.: Genetic Psych. Monographs, 1961), pp. 399–400.

10. Alfred Ernest Crawley, *The Mystic Rose: A Study of Primitive Marriage* (New York, 1902), p. 90.

11. Meggitt, "Male-Female Relationships in the Highlands of Australian New Guinea."

12. Hutton Webster, *Taboo, A Sociological Study* (Stanford: Stanford University Press, 1942), p. 87.

13. Pliny, *Natural History*, trans. H. Rackham (Cambridge: Harvard University Press, 1961), book 7, p. 549.

14. E. Novak, "The Superstition and Folklore of Menstruation," *Johns Hopkins Hospital Bulletin* 27 (1916).

15. Margaret Mead, *Male and Female* (New York: Morrow, 1949), p. 222.

16. Crawley, *The Mystic Rose: A Study of Primitive Marriage*, p. 149.

17. Sir James George Frazer, *The Golden Bough*, 1 vol. abr. ed. (New York: Macmillan, 1953), p. 206.

18. L. Deslange, *Le Plateau Central Nigerian* (Paris, 1904), p. 227.

19. Webster, *Taboo, A Sociological Study*, p. 83.

20. Webster, *Taboo, A Sociological Study*, p. 87.

21. H. R. Hays, *The Dangerous Sex: The Myth of Feminine Evil* (New York: Putnam, 1965), p. 279.

22. Webster, *Taboo, A Sociological Study*, pp. 83–85.

23. Simone de Beauvoir, *The Second Sex* (New York: Knopf, 1952), p. 138.

24. Cited in C. Frederic Fluhmann, *Menstrual Disorders: Pathology, Diagnosis and Treatment* (Philadelphia and London: Saunders, 1939). Schick's experiment is described more fully in Fritz Vosselmann, *La Menstruation: Lègendes, Coutumes et Superstitions* (Lyon, 1935).

25. William Freeman and Joseph M. Looney, with the technical assistance of Rose R. Small, "Studies on the Phytotoxic Index II. Menstrual Toxin ('menotoxin')," *Journal of Pharmacology and Experimental Therapeutics* 52 (1934).

26. Cited in Earl T. Engle, ed., *Menstruation and Its Disorders* (Springfield, Ill.: Thomas, 1950), pp. 187–205 and pp. 207–231.

27. Webster, *Taboo, A Sociological Study*, p. 86.

28. N. N. Bhattacharyya, *Indian Puberty Rites* (Calcutta, 1968), p. 19.

29. Frazer, *The Golden Bough*, p. 145.

30. Mead, *Male and Female*, p. 182.

31. Frazer, *The Golden Bough*, Third edition, unabridged (New York, 1935), vol. 10, p. 27.

32. Reik, *Pagan Rites in Judaism*, p. 81.

33. Crawley, *The Mystic Rose: A Study of Primitive Marriage*, p. 198.

34. Hays, *The Dangerous Sex: The Myth of Feminine Evil*, pp. 67–68.

CHAPTER 2. "NOT TONIGHT, DEAR": TABOOS OF SEX

1. This idea was first suggested to us by Nancy Scheper-Hughes, "Woman as Witch," *Popular Psychology*, no. 4 (1973).

2. William N. Stephens, *A Cross-cultural Study of Menstrual Taboos* (Provincetown, Mass.: Genetic Psych. Monographs, 1961), p. 401.

3. J. M. Rodwell, trans., *The Koran* (London: Dent, 1953), p. 363.

4. Isser Yehuda Unterman, "Family Purity: Its Wide Implications," reprinted in *Israel Magazine* 4 (January 1972): 68–74.

5. Cited in Ben Barker-Benfield, "The Spermatic Economy: A Nineteenth Century View of Sexuality," *Feminist Studies* 1 (Summer 1972): 45–74.

6. Soranus, *Gynecology*, trans. Owsei Temkin (Baltimore: Johns Hopkins University Press, 1956), p. 35.

7. William S. Sadler and Lena K. Sadler, *Living a Sane Sex Life* (Chicago: Follett, 1938), p. 243.

8. Isidor Silberman, "A Contribution to the Psychology of Menstruation," *International Journal of Psychoanalysis* 31 (1950): 260.

9. Hutton Webster, *Taboo, A Sociological Study* (Stanford: Stanford University Press, 1942), pp. 82, 130.

10. Chester B. Martin, Jr., and Eugene M. Long, Jr., "Sex during the Menstrual Period," *Medical Aspects of Human Sexuality* 3 (1969): 40.

11. Fritz Vosselmann, *La Menstruation: Lègendes, Coutumes et Superstitions* (Lyon, 1935), p. 79.

12. Fred P. Robbins, "Psychosomatic Aspects of Dysmenorrhea," *American Journal of Obstetrics and Gynecology* 66 (1953): 808–815.

13. Mary Jane Sherfey, "A Theory of Female Sexuality," in *Sisterhood Is Powerful,* ed. Robin Morgan (New York: Random House, 1970), p. 221.

14. Mary E. Luschen and David Pierce, in "Effect of the Menstrual Cycle on Mood and Sexual Arousability," *Journal of Sex Research* 8 (February 1972): 41–47, found through studying women's reactions to pictures of sexually attractive males that women are more easily aroused during ovulation than during menstruation.

15. William H. Masters and Virginia E. Johnson, *Human Sexual Inadequacy* (Boston: Little, Brown, 1970), p. 221. This finding has been supported by others in the field.

16. Silberman, "A Contribution to the Psychology of Menstruation," p. 260.

17. T. O. Beidelman, "Pig (Guluwe): An Essay on Ngulu Sexual

Symbolism and Ceremony," *Southwestern Journal of Anthropology* 20 (1964): 375.

18. L. M. Terman, *Psychological Factors in Marital Happiness* (New York: McGraw-Hill, 1938), cited in Martin and Long, "Sex during the Menstrual Period," p. 40.

19. William H. Masters and Virginia E. Johnson, *Human Sexual Response* (Boston: Little, Brown, 1966), p. 26.

20. Katharina Dalton, *The Menstrual Cycle* (New York: Pantheon, 1971), p. 26.

21. Unterman, "Family Purity: Its Wide Implications," p. 70.

22. Webster, *Taboo, A Sociological Study*, p. 82.

23. *Tits & Clits*, produced by Lyn Chevli and Joyce Sutton (Laguna Beach, Calif., 1972).

24. Martin and Long, "Sex during the Menstrual Period," p. 43.

25. Cited in Webster, *Taboo, A Sociological Study*, pp. 105, 220n.

26. Karen Paige, "Women Learn to Sing the Menstrual Blues," *Psychology Today*, September 1973, pp. 43–44.

27. Martin and Long, "Sex during the Menstrual Period," pp. 43–46.

28. Paige, "Women Learn to Sing the Menstrual Blues," p. 43.

29. Martin and Long, "Sex during the Menstrual Period," p. 43.

CHAPTER 3. PUTTING HER IN HER PLACE: RITES OF THE MENARCHE

1. Ruth Benedict, *Patterns of Culture* (Boston: Houghton Mifflin, 1944), pp. 28–29.

2. Sir James George Frazer, *The Golden Bough*, 1 vol. abr. ed. (New York: Macmillan, 1953), pp. 690–691.

3. George Devereaux, "The Psychology of Feminine Genital Bleeding," *International Journal of Psychoanalysis* 31 (1950): 242–243.

4. Frazer, *The Golden Bough*, p. 695.

5. Frazer, *The Golden Bough*, p. 698.

6. N. N. Battacharyya, *Indian Puberty Rites* (Calcutta, 1968), p. 16.

7. Frazer, *The Golden Bough*, p. 693.

8. Devereaux, "The Psychology of Feminine Genital Bleeding," pp. 242–243.

9. Frazer, *The Golden Bough*, p. 696.

10. Frazer, *The Golden Bough*, p. 703.

11. Karen Paige, "Women Learn to Sing the Menstrual Blues," *Psychology Today* (September 1973).

12. Mary Douglas, *Purity and Danger: An Analysis of Concepts of Pollution and Taboo* (New York: Praeger, 1966), p. 116.

13. Charlotte Frisbie, *Kinaalda: A Study of the Navaho Girl's Puberty Ceremony* (Middletown, Conn.: Wesleyan University Press, 1967), p. 350; and Devereaux, "The Psychology of Feminine Genital Bleeding," p. 242.

14. Bhattacharyya, *Indian Puberty Rites*, p. 6.

15. Frazer, *The Golden Bough*, p. 24.

16. Bhattacharyya, *Indian Puberty Rites*, p. 8.

17. Bhattacharyya, *Indian Puberty Rites*, p. 20.

18. Bruno Bettelheim, *Symbolic Wounds: Puberty Rites and the Envious Male* (New York: Collier, 1962), p. 172.

19. Frazer, *The Golden Bough*, p. 693.

20. Devereaux, "The Psychology of Feminine Genital Bleeding," p. 246.

21. Simone de Beauvoir, *The Second Sex* (New York: Knopf, 1952), p. 141.

22. *The Ante-Nicene Fathers: Translation of the Writing of the Fathers Down to A.D. 325*, vol. 3 (Baltimore, 1885), p. 688.

23. Frazer, *The Golden Bough*, p. 61.

24. Hutton Webster, *Taboo, A Sociological Study* (Stanford: Stanford University Press, 1942), p. 88.

25. Webster, *Taboo, A Sociological Study*, pp. 90–91.

26. Marie Smith, "Menstrual Disorders" (Ph.D. diss., University of Denver, 1971), p. 47.

27. H. R. Hays, *The Dangerous Sex: The Myth of Feminine Evil* (New York: Putnam, 1965), p. 51.

28. Bettelheim, *Symbolic Wounds: Puberty Rites and the Envious Male*, pp. 143–145.

29. C. Beals, "Sex Life in Latin America," in *The Encyclopedia of Sexual Behavior*, eds. A. Ellis and A. Abarbanel, vol. 2 (New York, 1961), pp. 600–601.

30. Bhattacharyya, *Indian Puberty Rites*, p. 29.

31. Frisbie, *Kinaaldá: A Study of the Navaho Girl's Puberty Ceremony*, p. 9.

32. Bhattacharyya, *Indian Puberty Rites*, p. 18.

33. Margaret Mead, *Male and Female* (New York: Morrow, 1949), p. 184.

34. Minda Borun et al., *Women's Liberation: An Anthropological View* (Pittsburgh, 1971), p. 7.

35. Judith K. Brown, "A Cross-cultural Study of Female Initiation Rites," *American Anthropologist* 65 (1963): 947.

CHAPTER 4. WOMAN UNCLEAN: MENSTRUAL TABOOS IN JUDAISM AND CHRISTIANITY

1. Bracha Sacks, "Why I Choose Orthodoxy," *Ms.* (July 1974).

2. Sr. Albertus Magnus McGrath, O.P., *What a Modern Catholic Believes about Women* (Chicago, 1972), p. 22.

3. McGrath, *What a Modern Catholic Believes about Women*, p. 22.

4. *Interpreter's Bible*, ed. Nolan B. Harmon (New York: Abingdon, 1953), p. 74.

5. Bede, *History of the English Church and People* (Baltimore: Penguin, n.d.), pp. 76–81.

6. D. M. Prumner, O.P., *Handbook of Moral Theology*, trans. G. W. Sheldon (Cork, 1963), p. 270.

7. McGrath, *What a Modern Catholic Believes about Women*, p. 110.

8. McGrath, *What a Modern Catholic Believes about Women*, p. 11, citing the *Proto-Evangelum of James*, an apochryphal book of the early Christians.

9. *Encyclopedia of Religion and Ethics*, ed. James Hastings (Edinburgh and New York, 1921), p. 574.

10. *Basic Writings of St. Thomas Aquinas*, ed. Anton C. Pegis (New York: Random House, 1948), p. 880.

11. *Malleus maleficarum*, trans. by Rev. Montague Summers (Great Britain: John Rodker, 1928), part 1.

12. *Malleus maleficarum*, part 1.

13. David Turner, *The Prodigal Daughter* as performed at the John F. Kennedy Center for the Performing Arts, Washington, D.C., November 12, 1973.

CHAPTER 5. MENSTRUATION AND MEDICAL MYTH

1. Aristotle, *On the Generation of Animals*, trans. A. L. Peck (London: Heinemann, 1943), 2. 4. 185. All other citations from this edition will be given in the text.

2. Pliny, *Natural History*, 7. 13, cited in G. Frederic Fluhmann, *Menstrual Disorders: Pathology, Diagnosis and Treatment* (Philadelphia and London: Saunders, 1939), p. 20.

3. Cited in Una Stannard, "Adam's Rib, or the Woman Within," *Transactions* 1 (1970): 27.

4. Fritz Vosselmann, *La Menstruation, Lègendes, Coutumes et Superstitions* (Lyon, 1935), p. 16.

5. Fluhmann, *Menstrual Disorders: Pathology, Diagnosis and Treatment*, p. 19.

6. Soranus, *Gynecology*, trans. Owsei Temkin (Baltimore: Johns Hopkins University Press, 1956), p. 23.

7. Vosselmann, *La Menstruation, Lègendes, Coutumes, et Superstitions*, pp. 16–17.

8. Fluhmann, *Menstrual Disorders: Pathology, Diagnosis and Treatment*, pp. 19–20.

9. John Freind, *Emmenologis*, trans. Thomas Dale (London, 1752), pp. 19, 67.

10. William Stephenson, *American Journal of Obstetrics* 15 (1882): 287–294.

11. G. Stanley Hall, *Adolescence*, vol. 1 (New York: Appleton, 1904), p. 487.

12. J. M. Tanner, "Growing Up," *Scientific American* 229 (1973): 43.

13. Soranus, *Gynecology*, p. 17.

14. Albertus Magnus, *Le Grand et le Petit Albèrt* (Paris, 1970), p. 70.

15. Hermann Heinrich Ploss, Max Bartels, and Paul Bartels, *Woman: An Historical Gynaecological and Anthropological Compendium*, ed. Eric John Dingwall (St. Louis: Mosby, 1936), p. 564.

16. Fluhmann, *Menstrual Disorders: Pathology, Diagnosis and Treatment*, p. 18.

17. August Bebel, *Woman and Socialism*, trans. Meta Stern (New York, 1910), p. 50. Bebel's work was originally published in 1883.

18. Pye Henry Chavasse, *Woman as a Wife and Mother* (Philadelphia, 1871), pp. 90–91.

19. Ploss, Bartels, and Bartels, *Woman: An Historical Gynaecological and Anthropological Compendium*, p. 573.

20. Fluhmann, *Menstrual Disorders: Pathology, Diagnosis and Treatment*, p. 34.

21. Quoted in C. L. Henton, "A Comparative Study of the Onset of Menarche among Negro and White Children," *Journal of Psychology* 46 (1958): 65.

22. Chavasse, *Woman as a Wife and Mother*, p. 89.

23. Ira Warren et al., *New Warren's Household Physician* (Boston, 1901), p. 381. This is a reissue of an earlier text.

24. The pro-blonde study is cited in Fluhmann, *Menstrual Disorders: Pathology, Diagnosis and Treatment*, p. 32; the redhead and brunette studies are reported in Ploss, Bartels, and Bartels, *Woman: An Historical Gynaecological and Anthropological Compendium*, pp. 573, 589.

25. Ploss, Bartels, and Bartels, *Woman: An Historical Gynaecological and Anthropological Compendium*, p. 567.

26. Ploss, Bartels, and Bartels, *Woman: An Historical Gynaeco-logical and Anthropological Compendium*, p. 581; and Hall, *Adolescence*, pp. 478–479.

27. James V. Ricci, *The Genealogy of Gynaecology* (Philadelphia: Blakiston, 1950), pp. 367–368.

28. Ploss, Bartels, and Bartels, *Woman: An Historical Gynaeco-logical and Anthropological Compendium*, p. 586.

29. Cilédin Chavasse, *Woman as a Wife and Mother*, pp. 90–91.

30. Cited in Marie Smith, "Menstrual Disorders" (Ph.D. diss., University of Denver, 1971), p. 9.

CHAPTER 6. MODERN MENSTRUAL POLITICS

1. U.S., Congress, Senate, *Congressional Record*, March 22, 1972, p. S4531.

2. Historical data on the women's rights movement of the nineteenth and early twentieth centuries come from Eleanor Flexner, *Century of Struggle: The Woman's Rights Movement in the United States* (Cambridge: Harvard University Press, 1959).

3. Edward H. Clarke, *Sex in Education* (1873), p. 45.

4. *Sex and Education: A Reply to Dr. E. H. Clarke's "Sex in Education*," ed. Julia Ward Howe (Boston, 1874: New York: Arno, 1972).

5. Azel Ames, Jr., *Sex in Industry* (Boston, 1875), p. 43.

6. Clelia Duel Mosher, *Health and the Woman Movement* (New York: Woman's Press, 1916), revised and expanded to *Woman's Physical Freedom* (New York: Woman's Press, 1923), p. 20.

7. Mosher, *Health and the Woman Movement*, p. 30.

8. Mary Putnam-Jacobi, *The Question of Rest for Women during Menstruation* (New York, 1877), p. 15.

9. Grace Naismith, *Private and Personal* (New York: McKay, 1966), p. 147.

10. Naismith, *Private and Personal*, p. 174.

11. The most thorough study of this subject we have found is "Two Contributions to the Experimental Study of the Menstrual Cycle," by the Great Britain Industrial Health Research Board, 1928.

12. Cited in David R. Zimmerman, "Medicine Today," in *Ladies' Home Journal*, (March 1974), p. 20. Three studies we have found useful in exploring the effects of athletics on the menstrual cycle are Theresa W. Anderson, "Swimming and Exercise during Menstruation," *Journal of Health, Physical Education and Recreation* (October 1965); Marjorie Phillips et al., "Sports Activity for Girls," *Journal of Health, Physical Education and Recreation* (De-

cember 1959); Grace Thwing, "Swimming during the Menstrual Period," *Journal of Health and Physical Education* (March 1943).

13. Maury Levy, "Mother Freedom," *Philadelphia,* January 1974, p. 100 ff.

CHAPTER 8. THE FIRST POLLUTION: PSYCHOANALYSIS
AND THE MENARCHE

1. Otto Fenichel, *The Psychoanalytic Theory of Neuroses* (New York: Norton, 1945), p. 11.

2. Sigmund Freud, *The Complete Psychological Works,* trans. James Strachey, vol. 1 (London: Hogarth, 1961), p. 390. All subsequent references to Freud are to this edition.

3. Mary Chadwick, *The Psychological Effects of Menstruation* (New York: Nervous & Mental Diseases, 1932), p. 33.

4. Helene Deutsch, *The Psychology of Women,* 2 vols. (New York: Grune, 1944), vol. 2, pp. 460–470. Further citations from Deutsch are from this edition.

5. Erik Erikson, *Identity: Youth and Crisis* (New York: Norton, 1968), p. 278.

6. Melanie Klein, *Papers on Psycho-Analysis,* 2d ed. (London, 1918), p. 560.

7. Klein, *Papers on Psycho-Analysis,* pp. 307–309.

8. Norman O. Brown, *Love's Body* (New York: Random House, 1966), p. 63.

9. Vivian Gornick and Barbara K. Moran (eds.), *Woman in Sexist Society* (New York: Basic Books, 1971), p. 18.

10. Chadwick, *The Psychological Effects of Menstruation,* pp. 28–35.

11. Karen Horney, *Feminine Psychology* (New York: Norton, 1967), pp. 78–79.

12. Clara M. Thompson, *Interpersonal Psychoanalysis: The Selected Papers of Clara M. Thompson,* ed. Maurice R. Green (New York: Basic Books, 1964), p. 305. Subsequent references are to this edition.

13. Natalie Shainess, "A Re-evaluation of Some Aspects of Feminity Through a Study of Menstruation: A Preliminary Report," *Comprehensive Psychiatry* 2 (1961): 24.

14. Fenichel, *The Psychoanalytic Theory of Neuroses,* pp. 411, 240.

15. Karen Horney, "The Problems of Feminine Masochism" (1933), in *Feminine Psychology,* pp. 232–233.

16. Horney, "The Problems of Feminine Masochism," pp. 234–241.

17. Thompson, *Interpersonal Psychoanalysis: The Selected Papers of Clara M. Thompson*, pp. 234–235.

18. Judith Kestenberg, "Menarche," in *Adolescents: A Psychoanalytic Approach to Problems and Therapy*, eds., Sandor Lorand and Henry Scheer (New York: Harper & Row, 1964), p. 34.

CHAPTER 9. THE STORM BEFORE THE CALM: THE PREMENSTRUAL SYNDROME

1. Karen Horney, "Premenstrual Tension," in *Feminine Psychology*, (New York: Norton, 1967), pp. 99–106; and Robert Frank, "The Hormonal Causes of Premenstrual Tension," *Archives of Neurology and Psychiatry* 26 (1931): 1053.

2. Katharina Dalton, *The Menstrual Cycle* (New York: Pantheon, 1971).

3. Judith Bardwick and Melville Ivey, *Psychology of Women* (New York: Harper & Row, 1971), pp. 30–33.

4. Karen Paige, "Women Learn to Sing the Menstrual Blues," *Psychology Today*, September 1973, pp. 41–46.

5. Horney, "Premenstrual Tension," in *Feminine Psychology*, pp. 99–106.

6. Therese Benedek, *Psychosexual Functions in Women* (New York: Ronald, 1952).

7. Mary Brown Parlee, "The Premenstrual Syndrome," *Psychological Bulletin* 80 (1973): 454–465.

8. K. Jean and R. John Lennane, "Alleged Psychogenic Disorders in Women—Possible Sexual Prejudice," *New England Journal of Medicine*, vol. 288, no. 6 (February 8, 1973), pp. 288–292. Cited in Parlee, "The Premenstrual Syndrome."

9. Other explanations locate the source of premenstrual discomfort in the pituitary gland, in the overproduction of desoxycorticosterone (DOC), or in the effects of monoamine oxidase upon the central nervous system. These theories are contained in "A Symposium on Premenstrual Tension," ed. Joseph H. Morton, in *International Record of Medicine* 166 (1953). This symposium contains the following essays: S. Charles Freed, "History and Causation of Premenstrual Tension," pp. 465–468; S. Leon Israel, "The Clinical Pattern and Etiology of Premenstrual Tension," pp. 469–474; Edward L. Suarez-Murias, "The Psychophysiologic Syndrome Premenstrual Tension with Emphasis on the Psychiatric Aspect," pp. 475–486; Harvey E. Billig, Jr., "The Role of Premenstrual Tension in Industry," pp. 487–491; Howard L. Oleck, "Legal Aspects of Premenstrual Tension," pp. 492–501; J. P. Greenhill, "The Treatment of

Premenstrual Tension by Electrolytes," pp. 502–504; Joseph H. Morton, "Treatment of Premenstrual Tension," pp. 505–510.

10. Quoted in Paige, "Women Learn to Sing the Menstrual Blues," p. 44, from a speech made by Berman in July 1970.

11. I. L. McKinnon, P. C. B. McKinnon, and A. D. Thompson, "Lethal Hazards of the Luteal Stage of the Menstrual Cycle," *British Medical Journal* 1 (1959): 1015–1017.

12. Katharina Dalton, "Menstruation and Crime," *British Medical Journal* 2 (1961): 1752.

13. Erna Wright, *Painless Menstrual Periods* (New York: Hart, 1968).

14. R. E. Whitehead, "Notes from the Department of Commerce: Women Pilots," *Journal of Aviation Medicine* 5 (1934): 47–49.

15. C. M. Tonks, "Attempted Suicide and the Menstrual Cycle," *Journal of Psychosomatic Research* 11 (1968): 319–323.

16. Richard D. Wetzel, James N. McClure, and Theodore Reich, "Premenstrual Symptoms in Self-Referrals to a Suicide Prevention Service," *British Journal of Psychiatry* 119 (1971): 525–526.

17. Ayres L. Ribero, "Menstruation and Crime," *British Medical Journal* 640 (1962).

18. A. Alvarez, *The Savage God: A Study of Suicide* (New York: Random House, 1972).

19. Emile Durkheim, *Suicide*, trans. John A. Spaulding and George Simpson (New York: Free Press, 1951), p. 341.

20. Edward B. Allen and George W. Henry, "The Relation of Menstruation to Personality Disorders," *American Journal of Psychiatry* 13 (1933): 239–276.

21. E. Y. Williams and L. R. Weekes, "Premenstrual Tension Associated with Psychotic Episodes," *Journal of Nervous and Mental Diseases* 116 (1952): 321–329.

22. Oleck, "Legal Aspects of Premenstrual Tension," pp. 492–501.

23. Irwin N. Peer, "Medical, Psychiatric and Legal Aspects of Premenstrual Tension," *American Journal of Psychiatry* 115 (1958): 211–219.

24. Aleta Wallach and Larry Rubin, "The Premenstrual Syndrome and Criminal Responsibility," *UCLA Law Review* 19 (1971): 210–312.

25. In the fall of 1973, Susan Lee of the Baltimore Women's Law Center directed a discussion of PMS and the law. According to Ms. Lee, the participants, most of them lawyers or law students, agreed that the issue should be studied more extensively before any move is made to gain it acceptance by the legal community. There was con-

cern that recognition of PMS as a defense might damage women, owing to the enormous confusion surrounding the syndrome.

26. Nancy Milford, in a review of Juliet Mitchell's *Woman's Estate, Partisan Review* (Winter 1973): 147–151.

27. Parlee, "The Premenstrual Syndrome," pp. 454–465.

28. Rudolf H. Moos, *Menstrual Distress Questionnaire: Preliminary Manual* (Department of Psychiatry, Stanford University School of Medicine, 1969). For a critique of the methods of the questionnaire, consult Parlee, "The Premenstrual Syndrome," pp. 454–465.

CHAPTER 10. "WHAT EVERY GIRL SHOULD KNOW"

1. *A Notebook of Intimate Problems* (New York, 1934), pp. 13–14, 97.

2. William S. Sadler, *A Doctor Talks to Teenagers* (St. Louis: Mosby, 1948), pp. 270–272.

3. Judy Blume, *Are You There God? It's Me, Margaret* (New York: Bradbury, 1970), pp. 94–97.

4. Boston Women's Health Collective, *Our Bodies, Ourselves: A Book By and For Women* (New York: Simon and Schuster, 1973), p. 15.

5. "Battle of the Badge: Philadelphia's Proposed Womanhood Badge," *Newsweek*, July 23, 1973.

CHAPTER 11. THE MONTHLY EUPHEMISM

1. Unless otherwise attributed, all expressions come from our own observations and those of friends (especially Jean Paris of Johns Hopkins University) or from two sources: Hermann Heinrich Ploss, Max Bartels, and Paul Bartels, *Woman: An Historical Gynaecological and Anthropological Compendium*, ed. Eric John Dingwall (St. Louis: Mosby, 1936), p. 588; and Natalie F. Joffe, "The Vernacular of Menstruation," *Word* 4 (1948): 181–186. Joffe's is the most complete discussion and the only study to focus directly on menstrual language. Later discussions of expressions add nothing to her listings.

CHAPTER 12. RED HUMOR: THE MENSTRUAL JOKE

1. Unless a book source is given, joke examples come from friends or personal memories or from two joke books: Anonymous, *Still More from Sex to Sexty* (Fort Worth, 1968) and Anonymous *Cupid Sex to Sexty* (Fort Worth, 1973).

2. Sigmund Freud, *Jokes and Their Relation to the Unconscious*, trans. James Strachey (New York: Norton, 1961), p. 97.

3. G. Legman, *The Rationale of the Dirty Joke* (New York: Grove, 1968), p. 684.

4. Marilyn Coffey, *Marcella* (New York: Charterhouse Books, 1973) p. 92.

CHAPTER 13. PERIODIC PARADE: MENSTRUATION IN ADVERTISING

1. Alice Munro, *Lives of Girls and Women* (New York: McGraw-Hill, 1972).

2. *Ladies' Home Journal*, May 1920, p. 190. Only one publication will be cited for each ad, although most ads run in several magazines simultaneously and for several months, if not years.

3. *Good Housekeeping*, January 1923, p. 137.

4. *Good Housekeeping*, February 1933, p. 167.

5. *Good Housekeeping*, January 1943, p. 153.

6. *Good Housekeeping*, June 1943, p. 100.

7. *Good Housekeeping*, April 1943, p. 174.

8. *Good Housekeeping*, May 1943, p. 103.

9. Betty Friedan, *The Feminine Mystique* (New York: Norton, 1963).

10. *Good Housekeeping*, February 1953, p. 14.

11. *Good Housekeeping*, February 1953, p. 129.

12. *Mademoiselle*, June 1970, p. 99.

13. *Mademoiselle*, June 1971, p. 34.

14. *Mademoiselle*, June 1967, p. 50.

15. *McCalls*, June 1967, p. 29.

16. *Cosmopolitan* January 1973, p. 72.

17. *McCalls*, October 1970, p. R-10.

18. *Ladies' Home Journal*, June 1973, p. 17.

19. Debbie Rewalt, "Trends in Advertising of Feminine Hygiene Products," unpublished paper supplied to us by James Brooks of Campana Corporation.

20. *Supermarket*, October 1972, p. 60.

21. *Supermarket*, October 1972, p. 60.

CHAPTER 14. RAGS TO RICHES: THE MENSTRUAL PRODUCTS INDUSTRY

1. William N. Stephens, *A Cross-Cultured Study of Menstrual Taboos* (Provincetown, Mass.: Genetic Psych. Monographs, 1961), p. 399.

2. H. Frederick Kilander, *Sex Education in the Schools* (London: Collier-MacMillan, 1970), pp. 267-270.

3. Eric Trimmer, *Femina* (New York: Stein & Day, 1966), p. 24.

4. Joseph A. Page, "What the FDA Won't Tell You about FDS," *The Washington Monthly*, vol. 5 (March 1973), pp. 19–25.

5. Alicia Bay Laurel, *Living on the Earth* (Berkeley, 1970).

6. Information on testing and research cited below is available from the following manufacturers: Campana Corp., Batavia, Ill. 60410; Kimberly-Clark Corp., N. Lake St., Neenah, Wisc. 54956; Personal Products Co., 501 George St., New Brunswick, N.J.; Tampax, Inc., 5 Dakota Dr., Lake Success, N.Y. 11040; Tassaway, Inc., 155 So. Robertson Blvd., Beverly Hills, Calif. 90211.

CHAPTER 15. MENSTRUATION GOES PUBLIC

1. Aaron Latham, "Tom Seaver in the Locker Room," *New York*, April 15, 1974, p. 39.

2. Blair Sabol, "Shooting from the Hip," *Village Voice*, July 4, 1974, p. 40.

3. Jill Johnston, "Living Heavily Ever After," *Village Voice*, January 24, 1974, p. 28.

4. "All in the Family," *New York Times*, February 24, 1974.

5. Interview with Jackie Gleason, *New York Times*, August 5, 1973.

6. "The Bloods" appears in *The Berkeley Music Collective Songbook*, and has been recorded by The Berkeley Women's Music Collective on Olivia Records. Both are available from Debbie Lempke, 2838 Mcgee Ave., Berkeley, Calif. 94703.

CHAPTER 16. THE BLEEDING TOWER: MENSTRUAL THEMES IN FAIRY TALES

1. *Grimm's Household Tales, with the Authors' Notes*, trans. Margaret Hunt (Detroit: Singing Tree, 1968); *The Juniper Tree and Other Tales from Grimm*, ed. Lore Segal and Maurice Sendak (New York: Farrar, Straus, 1973).

2. Wolfgang Lederer, *The Fear of Women* (New York: Grune, 1968), p. 200.

3. Lederer, *The Fear of Women*, p. 200.

4. Arland Ussher and Carl von Metzradt, *Enter These Enchanted Woods: An Interpretation of Grimm's Fairy Tales* (Dublin, 1966), pp. 9–10.

5. Thirteen is an unlucky number because of its association with women: There are thirteen "moons" in a calendar year and thirteen menstrual periods.

CHAPTER 17. ABSENT LITERATURE: THE MENARCHIE

1. Works cited in this chapter were used in the following editions:
Edmond de Goncourt, *Chérie* (Paris: Charpentier, 1884); Emile Zola, *La Joie de Vivre* ("Zest for Life"), trans. Jean Stewart (London: Elek, 1955); Collette Audry, *Aux Yeux de Souvenir* (1947), quoted in Simone de Beauvoir, *The Second Sex* (New York: Knopf, 1952), p. 295; Emma Goldman, *Living My Life*, vol. 1 (New York: Dover, 1970), p. 21; *A Young Girl's Diary*, preface by Sigmund Freud, trans. Eden and Cedar Paul (New York: Thomas Seltzer, 1923); Mary McCarthy, *Memories of a Catholic Girlhood* (New York: Harcourt Brace Jovanovich, 1957), pp. 131–134; Anne Frank, *The Diary of a Young Girl* (New York: Pocket Books, 1953), p. 115; Thyde Monnier, *Moi* (1949), quoted in de Beauvoir, *The Second Sex*, p. 292; Radclyffe Hall, *The Well of Loneliness* (London: Hammond, 1956), p. 83; Christopher Morley, *Kitty Foyle* (Philadelphia: Lippincott, 1939), p. 37; Betty Smith, *A Tree Grows in Brooklyn* (New York: Harper, 1943), pp. 194–195; Rumer Godden, *Greengage Summer* (New York: Viking, 1958), p. 167; Jay Kennedy, *Prince Bart* (New York: Farrar, Straus and Young, 1953), p. 287; Ella Leffland, *Mrs. Munck* (New York: Pocket Books, 1970), p. 21; Joyce Carol Oates, *them* (Greenwich: Fawcett, 1969), p. 157; Margaret Embry, *Shadi* (New York: Holiday House, 1971), p. 12; Toni Morrison, *The Bluest Eye* (New York: Pocket Books, 1970), pp. 25–28; Penelope Street, "The Magic Apple," in *Best American Short Stories of 1972*, ed. Martha Foley (Boston: Houghton Mifflin, 1973), p. 309; Peter Marks, *Hangups* (New York: Random House, 1973), pp. 141–142; Julia Whedon, *Girl of the Golden West* (New York: Charterhouse, 1973), p. 105; Sandra Hochman, *Walking Papers* (New York: Ballantine, 1971), p. 60; Lois Gould, *Such Good Friends* (New York: Dell, 1970), p. 107; Alix Kates Shulman, *Memoirs of an Ex-Prom Queen* (New York: Knopf, 1972), p. 41; Judy Blume, *Are You There God? It's Me, Margaret* (New York: Dell, 1970) passim.

CHAPTER 18. THE MIRACLE OF BLOOD: MENSTRUAL IMAGERY IN MYTH AND POETRY

1. Claude Dagmar Daly, "The Menstruation Complex in Literature," *Psychoanalytic Quarterly* 42 (1935): 307–340.
2. Clark Griffith, *The Long Shadow: Emily Dickinson's Tragic Poetry* (Princeton: Princeton University Press, 1964).
3. Quoted material in this chapter comes from the following sources: Victoria Woodhull is quoted in Page Smith, *Daughters of*

the Promised Land: Women in American History (Boston: Little, Brown, 1970); Emily Dickinson, *The Complete Poetry of Emily Dickinson*, ed. Thomas Johnson (Boston: Little, Brown, 1960); Tiamat myth in Padraic Colum, *Orpheus: Myths of the World* (New York: Macmillan, 1930); *Collected Poems of Edna St. Vincent Millay*, ed. Norma Millay (New York: Harper, 1956); Nadine MacDonald from *Currents: Concerns and Composition*, ed. Thomas E. Sanders (Beverly Hills: Glencoe, 1971), quoted with permission of editor and Glencoe Press; Persephone myths in Ovid, *Metamorphoses*, trans. Frank Justus Miller, vol. 1, book V, a bilingual edition first published 1916 (Cambridge: Harvard University Press, 1966) and in Thomas Bulfinch, *The Age of Fable* (New York: Heritage, 1942); Baudelaire, *Flowers of Evil: A Selection*, ed. Martheil and Jackson Mathews, a bilingual text (New York: New Directions, 1955); Sylvia Plath, *The Colossus* (New York: Knopf, 1962), *Ariel* (New York: Harper & Row, 1968), *Crossing the Water* (New York: Harper & Row, 1971), *Winter Trees* (New York: Harper & Row, 1972); Anne Sexton, *To Bedlam and Part Way Back* (Boston: Houghton Mifflin, 1960), *Live or Die* (Boston: Houghton Mifflin, 1966), *Transformations* (Boston: Houghton Mifflin, 1972); *The Collected Poems of W. B. Yeats* (New York: Macmillan, 1956); Adrienne Rich, *The Will to Change* (New York: Norton, 1971); Muriel Rukeyser, in *No More Masks!* ed. Ellen Bass and Florence Howe (New York, 1973).

4. Sigmund Freud, *The Interpretation of Dreams*, trans. A. A. Brill (New York: Random House, 1950). pp. 208–209, 236–237.

5. Winifred Richmond, *The Adolescent Girl: A Book for Parents and Teachers* (New York: Macmillan, 1925), p. 21; and Hutton Webster, *Rest Days: A Study in Early Law and Morality* (New York: Macmillan, 1916), p. 128.

6. Richmond, *The Adolescent Girl: A Book for Parents and Teachers*, p. 5.

7. C. G. Seligmann, *Reports on the Cambridge Anthropological Expedition to Torres Straits*, cited in Webster, *Rest Days: A Study in Early Law and Morality*, p. 128.

8. Fritz Vosselmann, *La Menstruation: Légendes, Coutumes et Superstitions* (Lyon, 1935), pp. 23–24.

CHAPTER 19. MENSTRUAL MADNESS IN DRAMA AND FICTION

1. Quoted material in this chapter comes from the following sources: August Strindberg, *Miss Julie*, trans. Elizabeth Sprigge (New York: Doubleday, 1965); Alison Lurie, *Love and Friendship* (New York: Macmillan, 1962); Clare Booth Luce, "A Dolls's House,"

Life, October 16, 1970; John Fowles, *The French Lieutenant's Woman* (Boston: Little, Brown, 1969); William Faulkner, *The Sound and the Fury* (New York: Random House, 1966) and *Light in August* (New York: Random House, 1967); Miguel de Cervantes, *Don Quixote*, trans. J. M. Cohen (Baltimore: Penguin, 1950); Dan Wakefield, *Going All the Way* (New York: Delacorte, 1970); Alix Kates Shulman, *Memoirs of an Ex-Prom Queen* (New York: Knopf, 1972); Brian Moore, *I Am Mary Dunne* (New York: Viking, 1968); Doris Lessing, *The Golden Notebook* (New York: Simon & Schuster, 1962); and Erica Jong, *Fear of Flying* (New York: Holt, 1973).

CHAPTER 20. FROM LEECHES TO ESTROGEN: THE MENOPAUSE AND MEDICAL OPTIONS

1. Charles Richard Gilbert, *Better Health for Women* (Garden City, N.Y.: Doubleday, 1964), p. 72.

2. Peter Curzen, "Eliminating the Menopause," *Practitioner* 208 (1972): 387.

3. G. Courtenay Beale, *Woman's Change of Life* (New York: Self-Science Institute, 1934), p. 46.

4. Cited by Andrew Currier, *The Menopause* (New York, 1897), p. 99.

5. Edward John Tilt, *The Change of Life in Health and Disease*, 2d ed. (London, 1857), p. 29.

6. Currier, *The Menopause*, pp. 153–154, 233–236.

7. Robert A. Wilson, *Feminine Forever* (New York: M. Evans, 1966), Wilson's book literally opened up the subject of menopause in popular magazines.

8. Tilt, *The Change of Life in Health and Disease*, p. 66.

9. Wilson, *Feminine Forever*, pp. 42, 84.

10. Kenneth Hutchin, *How Not to Kill Your Wife* (New York: Hawthorn, 1965), p. 188.

11. Bernice Neugarten, "A New Look at Menopause," *The Female Experience* (Del Mar, Calif., 1973), pp. 39–44.

12. William E. Easterling, "Managing the Menopause," *American Family Physician* 73 (1973): 137–142. Recent research has been conducted to establish a possible connection between menopause and cancer; none of it, however, is conclusive. See Kadhim Mohammed Al-Issa, "Maturation Index in Post-menopausal Risk and other Risk Factors to Recurrence of Carcinoma of the Breast," *Am. L. Epidemiol.* 96 (1972): 173–182; Gilliam Frere, "Mean Age at Menopause and Menarche in South Africa," *S. Afr. J. Med. Sci.* 36 (1971): 21–24. For a less recent but more comprehensive assessment of the menopause-cancer relationship, see Sherwin S. Kaufman, *The Age-*

less Woman: Menopause, Hormones, and the Quest for Youth (Englewood Cliffs, N.J.: Prentice-Hall, 1967).

13. Wilson, *Feminine Forever*, pp. 130–139.

14. Tilt, *The Change of Life in Health and Disease*, pp. 52–91.

15. Currier, *The Menopause*, p. 249.

16. Curzen "Eliminating the Menopause," p. 387.

17. M. E. Schleyer-Saonders, "Une Nouvelle Conception du Climactera," *Gynecol. Prac.*, 22 (1971): 493–500.

CHAPTER 21. PSYCHOLOGY AND THE MENOPAUSAL MENACE

1. See the chapter "Disease of the Cerebro-Vascular System," in Edward John Tilt, *The Change of Life in Health and Disease*, 2d ed. (London, 1857).

2. Sigmund Freud, *Complete Psychological Works*, trans. James Strachey (London: Hogarth, 1961), vol. 3, vol. 23, 226; quoted by Isidor Silberman, "A Contribution to the Psychology of Menstruation," *International Journal of Psycho-Analysis* 31 (1950): 266.

3. Helene Deutsch, *Psychology of Women*, 2 vols. (New York: Grune, 1944). See especially vol. 2, pp. 460–470, on the climacteric.

4. Erik Erikson, *Identity: Youth and Crisis* (New York: Norton, 1968), p. 278.

5. Joseph C. Rheingold, *The Fear of Being a Woman: A Theory of Maternal Destructiveness* (New York: Grune, 1964), pp. 492–501.

6. William S. Sadler and Lena K. Sadler, *Living a Sane Sex Life* (Chicago: Follett, 1938), p. 296.

7. Morton M. Hunt, *Her Infinite Variety: The American Woman as Lover, Mate and Rival* (New York: Harper, 1962), pp. 189–190.

8. Philip Wylie, *Generation of Vipers* (New York: Holt 1955, originally published in 1942), pp. 196–199.

9. Simone de Beauvoir, "From Maturity to Old Age," *The Second Sex* (New York: Knopf, 1968), pp. 541–561. Originally published in France by Librairie Gallimard, 1949. Earlier in the book, de Beauvoir claims for the menopausal woman a new health and vigor (p. 28). Generally, however, her attitude is negative.

10. Clara M. Thompson, *Interpersonal Psychoanalysis: The Selected Papers of Clara M. Thompson*, ed. Maurice R. Green (New York: Basic Books, 1964), p. 339.

11. George Devereux, "The Psychology of Feminine Genital Bleeding: An Analysis of Mohave Indian Puberty and Menstrual Rites," *International Journal of Psycho-Analysis* 31 (1950): 168.

12. Quoted by Carroll Smith-Rosenberg, "Puberty to Menopause: The Cycle of Femininity in Nineteenth-Century America,"

Feminist Studies 1 (1973): 58–72. Smith-Rosenberg quotes from a number of sources, including the diary of Elizabeth Drinker.

13. Ann Garlin Spencer, *Woman's Shares in Social Culture* (Philadelphia: Lippincott, 1925).

14. Clelia Mosher, *Health and the Woman Movement* (New York: Woman's Press, 1916), pp. 46–49.

15. Video tape, "Well-kept Secrets Revealed: Women's Experience with Changes of Life," produced by Feminist Women's Workshop, California Institute of the Arts. Distributed by Vision Quest, Inc.

16. Bernice Neugarten, "A New Look at Menopause," *The Female Experience* (Del Mar, Calif., 1973), pp. 39–44.

17. "Menopause at 33," *Good Housekeeping*, October 1973, p. 16 ff.

CHAPTER 22. "NOVEMBER OF THE BODY": THE MENOPAUSE AND LITERATURE

1. Quoted material in this chapter comes from the following sources: Mary Jane Lupton, *Elizabeth Barrett Browning* (Baltimore: Feminist Press, 1972); William Faulkner, *Light in August* (New York: Random House, 1967); Jack London, "Samuel," reprinted from *Moon Face* in Anne Fremantle's *Mothers: A Catholic Treasury of Great Stories* (New York: Ungar, 1951); Lillian Smith, *Strange Fruit* (New York: Harcourt, Brace, 1944); Nancy Milford, *Zelda* (New York: Harper & Row, 1970); John O'Hara, *The Ewings* (New York: Random House, 1972); Doris Lessing, *The Summer Before the Dark* (New York: Simon & Schuster, 1973); Tennessee Williams, *The Roman Spring of Mrs. Stone* (New York: New Directions, 1969); Angus Wilson, *The Middle Age of Mrs. Eliot* (New York: Harper & Row, 1959); James Joyce, *Ulysses* (New York: Modern Library, 1940); Thomas Mann, *The Black Swan* (New York: Knopf, 1954); Betty Smith, *A Tree Grows in Brooklyn* (New York: Harper, 1947); *No More Masks!* ed. Florence Howe and Ellen Bass (Garden City, N.Y.: Doubleday, 1973); Henry Miller, *Tropic of Cancer* (New York: Grove, 1970); May Sarton, *Mrs. Stevens Hears the Mermaids Singing* (New York: Nortonn 1965); Homer, *The Odyssey*, trans. Robert Fitzgerald (Garden City, N.Y.: Doubleday, 1961); Geoffrey Chaucer, *The Canterbury Tales: A Selection*, ed. Donald R. Howard and James M. Dean (New York: New American Library, 1969).

CHAPTER 23. THE MENSTRUAL HALL OF FAME

1. Jules Michelet, *Joan of Arc* (Ann Arbor: University of Michigan Press, 1957), p. 9.

2. Eleanor Flexner, *Century of Struggle: The Woman's Rights Movement in the United States* (New York: Atheneum, 1968), p. 11.

3. Emery Battis, *Saints and Sectaries* (Chapel Hill, N.C.: University of North Carolina Press, 1962), *passim*.

4. Emma Goldman, *Living My Life*, vol. 1 (New York: Peter Smith, 1970), pp. 57–61.

5. André Maurois, *Lélia: The Life of George Sand*, trans. Gerard Hopkins (New York: Harper, 1953), p. 94.

6. Virginia Woolf, *A Writer's Diary*, ed. Leonard Woolf (New York: Harcourt, Brace, 1954).

7. Victoria Lincoln, *A Private Disgrace: Lizzie Borden by Daylight* (New York: Putnam 1967).

CHAPTER 24. MOVING THE MENSES, OR VICARIOUS MENSTRUATION

1. S. L. Israel, *Diagnosis and Treatment of Menstrual Disorders and Sterility*, 4th ed. (New York: Harper & Row, 1967), p. 213.

2. J. M. Dunn, "Vicarious Menstruation," *American Journal of Obstetrics and Gynecology* 114 (1972): pp. 568.

3. C. Frederic Fluhmann, *The Management of Menstrual Disorders* (Philadelphia: Saunders, 1956), p. 132.

4. Fluhmann, *The Management of Menstrual Disorders*, pp. 288–289; Dunn, "Vicarious Menstruation," pp. 568–569.

5. J. T. Gordon, "An Unusual Case of Vicarious Menstruation," *American Journal of Obstetrics* 15 (1882): 343–344.

6. Marie Allen Smith, "Menstrual Disorders: Incidence and Relationship to Attitudes, Manifest Needs, and Scholastic Achievement in College Freshmen Women" (Ed. D. diss., University of Denver, 1970), p. 21.

CHAPTER 25. ESCAPING THE MONTHLIES

1. Germaine Greer, *The Female Eunuch* (New York: McGraw-Hill, 1971), p. 42.

2. George Starr White, *The Emancipation of Women, or Regulating the Duration of the Menses* (Los Angeles: Privately printed, 1934), p. 27 and *passim*.

3. Ira Warren et al., *New Warren's Household Physician* (Boston, 1901), p. 395.

4. White, *The Emancipation of Women*, p. 31.

5. The methadone study was done by R. C. Wallach, G. Blinick, and E. Jerez, in "Pregnancy and Menstrual Function in Narcotics Addicts Treated with Methadone: the Methadone Maintenance

Treatment Program," *American Journal of Obstetrics and Gynecology* 105 (1969): 1226. The study of those withdrawing without methadone was by Sheldon Stoffer, in "A Gynecologic Study of Drug Addicts," *American Journal of Obstetrics and Gynecology* 101 (1968): 779–783.

6. Dr. Shelton's views are published by the American Natural Hygiene Society, 1920 Irving Park Road, Chicago, Ill. 60613.

7. John Hersey, "Hiroshima," *New Yorker*, August 31, 1946, p. 50.

8. The tape, about ninety minutes long, is available from the Los Angeles Women's Health Center, 746 South Crenshaw, Los Angeles, Calif. 90005, for $100.

9. Ellen Frankfort, *Vaginal Politics* (New York: Quadrangle, 1973), pp. 193–201.

CHAPTER 26. SAIGNADE: SIMULATED MENSTRUATION IN THE MALE

1. Mary Ellmann, *Thinking About Women* (New York: Harcourt, Brace, 1970), pp. 17–19.

2. Cited in M. J. Meggitt, "Male-Female Relationships in the Highlands of Australian New Guinea," *American Anthropologist* 66 (1964).

3. Bruno Bettelheim, *Symbolic Wounds: Puberty Rites and the Envious Male* (New York: Collier, 1962), p. 19.

4. Joseph Campbell, *The Masks of God* (New York: Viking, 1959), pp. 59–60.

5. Elizabeth Gould Davis, *The First Sex* (Baltimore: Penguin, 1972), pp. 101–104.

6. Bettelheim, *Symbolic Wounds: Puberty Rites and the Envious Male*, p. 106.

7. M. F. Ashley-Montagu, "The Origin of Subincision in Australia," *Oceania* 8 (1937): 204.

8. Gésa Róhcim, "The Symbolism of Subincision," *American Imago* 6 (1949): 321–325.

9. Jules Michelet, *Journal* (Paris, 1962), *passim*.

CHAPTER 27. CYCLES AND RHYTHM IN MEN

1. Dr. Estelle Ramey, the most important writer about male cycles, translated the characteristic remark "that's just like a woman" into modern scientific terms: "This female manfests the characteristic cerebral defects of the XX chromosomal behavior determinants. She is largely restricted to decision making via limbic system–

hypothalamic neuronal pathways with little evidence of neocortical influences. Therefore, she is more accurately classified as *Homo emotionalis* or *Homo gonadis.*" See Ramey's "Sex Hormones and Executive Ability," in "Successful Women in the Sciences: An Analysis," *Annals of the New York Academy of Sciences* 208 (1973): 237–245; and her "Men's Cycles (They Have Them Too, You Know)," *Ms.* (Spring 1972): 8, 11–12, 14. This article is one of the best summaries of research on the subject.

2. Schmey, "Zur Theorie den Menstruation u. 2. Behandlung einiger Mens. Störungen," *Therapeut. Monatshefte* (1897), 93, cited in G. Stanley Hall, *Adolescence* (New York: Appleton, 1904), p. 489.

3. Hersey's work is discussed in Gay Luce, *Biological Rhythms in Psychiatry and Medicine* (New York: Dover, 1970), pp. 110–111.

4. Luce, *Biological Rhythms in Psychiatry and Medicine*, p. 111.

5. Luce, *Biological Rhythms in Psychiatry and Medicine*, p. 111.

6. Katharina Dalton, *The Menstrual Cycle* (New York: Pantheon, 1969), pp. 134–136.

7. Dalton, *The Menstrual Cycle*, pp. 105–107.

8. Dalton, *The Menstrual Cycle*, pp. 109–111.

9. Fliess's work is discussed in Luce, *Biological Rhythms in Psychiatry and Medicine*, p. 8.

CONCLUSION: LIFTING THE CURSE

1. K. F. Wellmann, "Menstruation, Pregnancy, and Birth in Prehistoric Rock Drawings of North America," *Deutsch. Med. Wochenschrift* 97 (1972): 1670–1671.

2. Bart Jordan, "Deciphering the Distant Past," *Publick Occurrences,* May 17, 1974, pp. 12–13.

3. Arlene Raven, "Faith Wilding: Chambers," *Womanspace* 3 (1973): 18–19.

4. "The Menses Is the Message," *Tits & Clits* (Laguna Beach, Calif., 1972).

INDEX